INVESTIGATIONS IN ENVIRONMENTAL SCIENCE

Unit 2: Energy Generation

A CASE-BASED APPROACH TO THE STUDY OF ENVIRONMENTAL SYSTEMS

Daniel C. Edelson Ph.D.

Developed by

The Geographic Data in Education (GEODE) Initiative
Northwestern University

In association with

HERFF JONES EDUCATION DIVISION

HERFF JONES EDUCATION DIVISION

84 Business Park Drive, Armonk, NY 10504 Phone (914) 273-2233
Fax (914) 273-2227 Toll Free (888) 698-TIME (8463) www.its-about-time.com

It's About Time, President
Tom Laster

**Director of Product
Development**
Barbara Zahm, Ph.D.

Creative/Art Director
John Nordland

Printed and bound in the United States of America.

ISBN-10: 1-58591-445-2

ISBN-13: 978-1-58591-445-6

2 3 4 5 VH 09 08 07

This material is based upon work supported by the National Science Foundation under
grants No. RED-9453715, ESI-9720687, DGE-9714534. Any opinions, findings, and conclusions or
recommendations expressed in this material are those of the author(s) and do not necessarily reflect
the views of the National Science Foundation.

Project Director
Daniel C. Edelson Ph.D.

Lead Curriculum Developers
Kathleen Schwille
Meridith Bruozas
Michael Lach
Michael Taber
Douglas Gordin

Curriculum Developers
Kylene Chinsio
Natalie Goldstein
Adam Tarnoff

**Lead Developer,
Teacher Edition**
Ann Rivet

**Developer,
Teacher Edition**
Amy Emmert

Consultants
Duane Griffin
Brad Sageman

Contributors
Janet Bell-Wehr
Jennifer Coyle
Matthew Cruz
Douglas Goodwin
Lisa Kenyon
Shanna McGarry
Petra Pancoskova
Cynthia Quinn
Colleen Riley
Marc Siciliano
Darlene Slusher
Craig Smith
Susan Trzaskus

**Pilot And
Field Test Teachers**
Janet Bell-Wehr
Lori Blackburn
Anne Bogardt
Staci Bynum
Patricia Carlson
Mollie David
Julie Dowling
Theresa Dzoga-Borg
Jayne Entihar
Roger Felch
Linda Fleming
Douglas Goodwin
Nina Hike-Teague
Lloyd Kiefer
Gloria Latta
Cynthia Lauster
Chris Nichols
Phyllis Nicholson
Lars Nelson
Danielle Oplaski
John Pritchard
Gwynna Reinhardt
Delvena Riggins-Dawes
Antoinette Rubalcaba
Cliff Schlund
Tamara Shibayama
Marc Siciliano
Julia Somers
Dawn Teaschner
Peter Thomas
Susan Trzaskus
Ray Tschillard
Eric Wheeler
Steve Wilson

Programmers
Brian Clark
Peter Moore
Eric Russell
Christopher Kadel
Ben Loh
Laura Ferguson
Hisham Petry

Geospatial Data Development
Terry Hammarquist
Michael Smith

**Undergraduate
Research Assistants**
Eddy Ameen
Tajuana Bates
Eric Hanson
Aaron Hosmon
Benjamin Johnson
Steve Juh
Danielle Lessovitz
Ray Liu
Michael Nam
Viktoria Wang

Evaluation
SRI International
Principal Investigators:
 Roy Pea
 William Penuel
Dan Zalles
Valerie Crawford
Yukie Toyama

The Learning Partnership
Principal Investigator:
Steven McGee

**WorldWatcher
Curriculum Project**
Daniel C. Edelson,
Principal Investigator
Louis M. Gomez,
Co-Principal Investigator

Unit Two Credits

Chapter 1: Electricity
LESSON 4: LOCAL POWER SOURCES (PAGE 33-4): United States and Wisconsin electricity generation information courtesy Energy Information Administration;

Chapter 2: Fossil Fuels
LESSON 1: HOW IS COAL FORMED? (PAGE 40): Swamp picture © 2000 Kentucky Geological Survey, University of Kentucky; (PAGE 41): How coal forms artwork by Stephen Greb, © 1997 Kentucky Geological Survey, University of Kentucky; (page 42): Different types of coal artwork by Stephen Greb, © 2000 Kentucky Geological Survey, University of Kentucky;
LESSON 3: BASICS OF COAL PLANTS (PAGE 59): Source: Tennessee Valley Authority;
LESSON 6: HISTORICAL ENERGY USE (PAGE 83): Photo of television courtesy of www.tvhistory.com;

Chapter 3: Impacts
LESSON 1: OTHER SOURCES OF EMISSIONS (PAGE 106): NOx and SOx emissions data in the United States from the Environmental Protection Agency's publication National Air Pollutant Emissions Trends: 1900-1998, (March 2000) EPA 454/R-00-002;
LESSON 3: BASICS OF ACID DEPOSITION (PAGE 121): pH tolerance chart courtesy of the Environmental Protection Agency;
LESSON 4: ECOSYSTEM IMPACTS (PAGE 136): Temperature and dissolved oxygen data from Alabaster, J.S. and Lloyd, R., 1980. Water quality for freshwater fish from Butterworth & Co. Ltd., London;
LESSON 5: WHY DO WE BURN COAL FOR ELECTRICITY? (PAGE 147): Wind patterns diagram courtesy the Natural Resources Defense Council;

Chapter 4: Plant Siting
LESSON 1: LAKE GENEVA, WISCONSIN (PAGE 158, 160): Lake Geneva area map and community statistics courtesy Lake Geneva Convention & Visitors Bureau, Lake Geneva Chamber of Commerce;
LESSON 2: LAND USE (PAGE 169): Arcview screenshots courtesy ESRI;

Chapter 5: Global Climate Change
LESSON 6: TEMPERATURE AND CARBON DIOXIDE (PAGE 239): changes in temperature and carbon dioxide levels for the past 160,000 years derived from ice core data, US Global Research Program;

Chapter 6: Alternative Energy
LESSON 2: LOCATION BACKGROUND (PAGE 267): Photograph of Albuquerque, New Mexico, courtesy Bernie Dodge, San Diego State University; (PAGE 268): Photograph of Burlington, Vermont, courtesy Karin Borei; (PAGE 269): Photograph of Laramie train courtesy Jason Lee Davis, Ph.D., Texas A&M University;
LESSON 2: LOCAL ENVIRONMENT (PAGE 271): Arcview Screenshots courtesy ESRI;
LESSON 3: BIOMASS ENERGY (PAGE 280): Photograph of hybrid poplars courtesy Segal Ranch, Grandview, Washington;
LESSON 3: HYDROELECTRIC ENERGY (PAGE 282): Photograph of Grand Coulee Dam in Grand Coulee, Washington, courtesy Bureau of Reclamation;
LESSON 3: SOLAR ENERGY (PAGE 284): Photograph of Photovoltaic panels courtesy National Renewable Energy Library.

Table of Contents

Chapter 1: Electricity 1

Lesson 1: The Demand for Energy 3
    1a: What are the Issues? 4
    1b: Stakeholders and Evidence 12

Lesson 2: What is Electricity? 15
    2a: Electricity Summary 16
    2b: Circuits 19

Lesson 3: Energy Transformations 21
    3a: Types of Energy 22
    3b: Converting Energy - Part 1 23
    3c: Converting Energy - Part 2 28
    3d: Technology to Transform Energy 29

Lesson 4: Large Scale Electricity Generation 30
    4a: Energy in the World 31
    4b: Local Power Sources 33

Chapter 2: Fossil Fuels 35

Lesson 1: What are Fossil Fuels? 37
    1a: Properties of Coal 38
    1b: How is Coal Formed? 40
    1c: Methods of Mining Coal 43
    1d: What are Fossil Fuels? 47

Lesson 2: Stored Energy 50
    2a: Stored Energy in a Peanut 51
    2b: Releasing Stored Energy 53
    2c: Improving Efficiency 55

Lesson 3: Power Plants 56
    3a: Virtual Tour 57
    3b: Basics of Coal Plants 59
    3c: Power Plant Inputs And Outputs 61
    3d: Sun to Electricity 62

Lesson 4: Operating a Power Plant 63
    4a: Operating a Power Plant 64
    4b: Demand in Different Seasons 67

Lesson 5: Improving Power Plant Efficiency 70
    5a: Efficiency Over Time 71
    5b: Percent Efficiency 73
    5c: Efficient Technology 74

Lesson 6: Consumer Energy Use 78
    6a: Energy Inventory 79
    6b: Historical Energy Use 82
    6c: How much is Reasonable? 85

Chapter 3: Impacts 87

Lesson 1: Combustion of Fossil Fuels 89
    1a: Side Effects 90
    1b: Combustion 93
    1c: Chemistry of Coal Combustion 95

1d: Modeling Combustion 100
1e: Coal Plant Operations 102
1f: Other Sources of Emissions 105
Lesson 2: Ash and Particulates **107**
2a: Collecting Particulates 108
2b: Particulate Danger 110
2c: Analyzing Particulates 112
2d: Ash and Particulate Emissions 113
2e: Mercury Bioaccumulation 115
Lesson 3: Acidic Deposition and Smog **118**
3a: Creating Acid Rain 119
3b: Basics of Acid Deposition 121
3c: Effects on Buildings 124
3d: Smog 127
Lesson 4: Water Impacts **130**
4a: Water Use by Power Plants 131
4b: Impacts of Water Use 133
4c: Ecosystem Impacts 136
Lesson 5: Dispersion of Impacts **138**
5a: Smokestacks 139
5b: Layers of Atmosphere 141
5c: Plumes and Dispersion 144
5d: Air Movement in Wisconsin 146
5e: Why Do We Burn Coal for Electricity? 148

Chapter 4: Plant Siting **153**
Lesson 1: Midwest Power **155**
1a: Midwest Power, Inc. 156
1b: Lake Geneva, Wisconsin 158
1c: Constraints 162
1d: Group Constraints & Considerations 163
Lesson 2: Exploring Lake Geneva **164**
2a: Lakes 165
2b: Land Use 167
2c: Roads and Railroads 171
2d: Narrowing Options 174
Lesson 3: Decision **175**
3a: Investigate Impacts 176
3b: Make a Decision 179
3c: Present Your Decision 180

Chapter 5: Global Climate Change **181**
Lesson 1: The Threat of Global Climate Change **183**
1a: What is Climate Change? 184
1b: Predicted Effects 186
1c: Uncertainty in Science 190
Lesson 2: Earth's Natural Temperature **195**
2a: Changing Temperature 196
2b: Temperature Over Time 202
Lesson 3: Sunlight and Temperature **204**
3a: Energy from the Sun 205
3b: Sunlight and Groundcover 207

Lesson 4: Predicting Temperatures **210**
    4a: Modeling the Earth's Temperature 211
    4b: What Should the Earth's Temperature Be? 216
    4c: Ocean Circulation, Albedo and Temperature 218

Lesson 5: Greenhouse Effect **221**
    5a: Atmospheric Gases 222
    5b: Greenhouse Effect 226
    5c: Modeling the Greenhouse Effect 230
    5d: Measuring Climate Change 235

Lesson 6: Carbon Dioxide **237**
    6a: Temperature and Carbon Dioxide 238
    6b: Global Carbon Cycle 240
    6c: Human Activities 242
    6d: Human Population and Carbon Dioxide 246

Lesson 7: Misconceptions **247**
    7a: Letters 248

Chapter 6: Alternative Energy 253
Lesson 1: What Are the Alternatives? **255**
    1a: What Are the Alternatives to Fossil Fuels? 256
    1b: Research 257
    1c: Five Alternatives 258
    1d: Alternative Energy Summary 262

Lesson 2: Setting the Stage **263**
    2a: Letter from NEPC 264
    2b: Location Background 266
    2c: Local Environment 270
    2d: Constraints 273
    2e: Group Constraints & Considerations 274

Lesson 3: Researching the Options **275**
    3a: Wind Energy 276
    3b: Biomass Energy 280
    3c: Hydroelectric Energy 282
    3d: Solar Energy 284
    3e: Nuclear Energy 286
    3f: Narrowing Options 288

Lesson 4: Decision **289**
    4a: Investigate Impacts 290
    4b: Make a Decision 293
    4c: Present Your Decision 294

Electricity

Chapter 1
Electricity

Connections

In Unit 1, you learned about growing populations and their increasing demand for resources. In this unit, the focus will be on energy as a resource, and how people meet the demand for energy by building power plants to generate electricity. You will learn how to help communities meet their growing electricity needs. In many areas of the country, populations are growing. This increases the demand for electricity. Your own community might have this problem, especially in the summer when air conditioning increases the demand for electricity. You will learn about increased energy demand in four U.S. communities and find a way to help them meet their needs. Your solution to their energy needs will be based on the communities' available resources, their goals, and the value that is placed on protecting the environment.

In this chapter:

In Chapter 1, you will be introduced to one community and the problems they are facing. You will look at electricity in detail. The information you will learn in this chapter, will help you make better decisions about the methods used to generate power. In the next chapter, you will explore the most common way electricity is generated – by burning fossil fuels.

When you're done you'll be able to:

- Describe the resources that are used in your own community to generate electricity.

- Describe energy transformations that might lead to useful power generation.

- Track energy through a transformation.

Lesson 1

The Demand for Energy

 Driving Question: *What are the consequences of the increase in demand for energy?*

Overview

In this lesson, you will learn about a problem facing many U.S. communities – electricity shortages. You will act out a news report from southeastern Wisconsin, where citizens are arguing about how to solve their electricity shortage problem. You will identify the stakeholders in the decision that needs to be made. You will learn about your role on a task force that will look into the community's electricity problem. You will also learn about how electricity is generated. And you will then make a decision about how the community can solve its electricity problem and protect the environment.

People's use of energy is increasing, but electricity generation often has adverse environmental effects. People have different views on these issues. Some people are more concerned about protecting the environment. Others believe that generating enough power for consumers is the most important goal. People's values will influence the environmental decisions made in their communities. Think about their concerns throughout this unit and form your own opinions about the decisions we face.

Important Content

- Almost everything we do requires electricity. Our lives and work are severely interrupted by brownouts and blackouts.

- There are many issues surrounding power generation including cost, land-use changes, efficiency considerations, sustainability for different environments, and byproducts generated.

What Are the Issues?

? *Essential Question:* Why do people disagree about how to meet the demand for energy?

Overview

In this activity, you will read a news report about a problem facing a growing region in southeastern Wisconsin. The community in the script is faced with the problem of meeting the energy demands of its growing population. Heat waves in the area have resulted in "brownouts." These are periods when the demand for electricity cannot be met and electrical service is reduced but not shut down. The area has also had "blackouts," or periods when the power went off completely. Adding a new power station seems like a simple solution for the community. However, there are complicated issues involved in deciding whether or not to build a power plant.

The end of the script describes a task force that you will join. The task force will research and plan a solution to the power problem in the Wisconsin community.

Procedure

Read the script *Electrical Dilemma* according to your teacher's instructions.

Analysis Question

1. Answer the essential question: *Why do people disagree about how to meet the demand for energy?*

Electrical Dilemma

Cast of Characters (and their roles)

(in order of appearance)

Genna Jemson	Reporter
Janice Nevins	Store owner
Peter Miller	County Nursing Home
Ella Gonzales	State Forest Conservation Alliance
Rev. William "Wild Billy" Biggs	Organization of Concerned Citizens
Miranda Hutcheson-Wade	Lakeside Home Owners Association
Anthony Chen	Wetland Preservation Society
Randy "my other car is a snowboard" Adams	Lifestyles for Sustainable Existence
Joan Gariboldi	Alternative Energy Alliance
Dr. Maya Barr	Genetics researcher

Scene - Noisy protesters are waving banners outside City Hall. A news reporter, Genna Jemson, stands in the crowd, reporting on the situation.

Genna Jemson, News Reporter -

To the audience:

The brownouts and power outages that have been sweeping across southeastern Wisconsin for the past several weeks have become a hot topic of controversy. Many here blame the power company, claiming that it has been ineffective in dealing with the power shortages. The power company has pointed out that the demand for power has been steadily increasing at a rate never seen before. To meet demand, the power company has been conducting "rolling" power outages, randomly selecting regions that will experience a brief shut-down in electricity. Occasionally, an area will experience a power outage for several hours or longer. The company contends that much of the increase in demand stems from recent growth in population and rapid economic development. For instance, the population in the six surrounding counties is projected to grow from 1 million in the year 2000 to 1.2 million in 2010. Although this amount of growth is common, it is alarming for many public utilities and social service providers within the community.

The question on everybody's mind today is: "How will the local government handle the increase in electrical demand from new housing, schools, industry, and commercial centers?" Although the obvious solution is to simply build another power plant, many citizens oppose the construction of any new power stations. Citizen opposition focuses on the difficulty of finding suitable locations, increasing concern about local water and air quality, and the threat of global

climate change.

Our local situation has become the focus of national attention. Community officials and regional power suppliers are struggling with the question of how to meet increasing energy needs in the most ecologically responsible way.

(Turning toward the crowd in front of City Hall)
It is obvious that these power outages have impacted our community on many levels. There are people gathered here in front of City Hall for many reasons. Let's find out what some community members have to say.

Janice Nevins is a local business owner. Janice, what has been your experience with the recent power outages?

Janice Nevins -
Well, I must say that all this is completely inexcusable. Last week, we experienced three blackouts, each one lasting longer than the one before. The latest outage lasted nearly eight hours! You see, I run a small grocery store just two blocks from here. You should stop by; we've just gotten a shipment of the most delicious melons. Well, anyway, during the last outage all my dairy products and all my meats spoiled! How am I supposed to provide my customers with the fresh food they need when I don't have electricity? Just to keep my refrigerators operating, I've been forced to buy a gas generator, which is much more expensive than you think!

Reporter -
Janice, what do you think City Hall should do?

Janice Nevins -
About City Hall, darling, don't even get me started! What have they done for me lately? Nothing, that's what! I don't care how the city plans to fix the problem, just as long as they fix it soon!

I think the government should have anticipated this problem years ago. They should have had the electric company plan ahead so that we all would have enough electricity. Why didn't they build more power plants before all those environmentalists took over everything? Now what are they going to do?

Reporter -
Ms. Nevins, do you think these power outages could have been prevented if people made more efforts to conserve energy?

Janice Nevins -
How am I supposed to know? I guess… maybe. But I need all my refrigerators! They are energy efficient, you know. I have the newest, state-of-the-art refrigerators. They save me lots of money because they do a pretty good job of keeping food cold. But a lot of good they do me now, with these darn power outages!

Reporter -

Thank you, Janice, for sharing your concerns with us. Nurse Peter Miller is from the County Nursing Home. Nurse Miller, how have the outages affected your patients and staff?

Nurse Miller -

This past week has been nothing but one disaster after another! I need a vacation! As you may have heard, the County Nursing Home, a full-care home for the elderly, has been without air conditioning for days now. Fortunately, we haven't had any heat-related deaths yet. Without A/C our patients run the risk of suffering from heat exhaustion or even heat stroke! We've moved some patients to a nearby cooling center but, as you can imagine, this exposes them to a whole other set of risks. The cooling center just doesn't have all the necessary medical equipment to support our patients. Even at the nursing home, medications that need to be refrigerated have spoiled and had to be thrown out after a blackout. I sure hope the local circuits will be fixed soon. Lives are at stake!

Reporter -

Mr. Miller, do you think these power outages could have been prevented in some way?

Nurse Miller -

I think that if we as citizens of the community curbed our energy use a little bit, that might have helped to prevent, or at least delay, these brownouts and outages. However, I do think that this may not be enough in the long run. City Hall needs to decide what to do about this now.

Reporter -

Thank you, Mr. Miller. Let's now turn our attention to some local special interest groups. These groups have been talking to the mayor for several weeks about how to best solve the energy crisis. First, we have Ms. Gonzales. Thank you for agreeing to speak with us, Ms. Gonzales. I understand that you're part of the State Forest Conservation Alliance. What are your group's major concerns regarding the recent power outages?

(SFCA) State Forest Conservation Alliance -
Ella Gonzales, Spokesperson -

Janice, I'm glad to have the chance to talk to you. Although we are not completely against building new power stations, we are concerned about conserving Wisconsin's natural forests. Even though the area of forested land in the state is increasing, the list of threatened and endangered species gets longer every year!

Our critics are fond of calling us "tree huggers." What they don't understand is that we don't just love the trees, we love the entire forest and all the creatures that live there! Should a traditional power station burning fossil fuels be built nearby? Emissions will surely create acid rain that could devastate the entire area!

Reporter -

Wait – isn't it true that the smokestacks on power plants carry the harmful emissions far away from the plant?

 **Electricity**

Gonzales -

That is true. Many of the emissions will travel far from the power plant and threaten the forests in other states. Even though the impacts might not be in Wisconsin, that doesn't make them any better!

In addition, fumes and noise pollution may have adverse effects on the nesting grounds of several endangered and threatened species that make their home in the forests right here in our state. If a power plant is truly necessary, we urge City Hall to look into more environmentally safe alternatives with minimal landscape disturbance. This landscape has evolved since the last Ice Age and should be preserved from the stressful impact of a power station.

Reporter -

So Ms. Gonzales, do you really love all the creatures of the forest?

Gonzales -

Why yes, of course.

Reporter -

All?

Gonzales -

(exasperated) Yes! All!

Reporter -

Even the big, gross, hairy spiders?

Gonzales -

Yes, Ms. Jemson, even the spiders.

Reporter -

(sounding disgusted) Yuck! I mean, uh, wow, that sure is wonderful. Well, thank you Ms. Gonzales.

We're standing now with Reverend William Biggs, the spokesperson for the Organization of Concerned Citizens. What are your group's major concerns regarding this issue?

(OCC) Organization of Concerned Citizens -
Rev. William "Wild Billy" Biggs, Spokesperson -

(*loudly*) We at OCC *understand* the needs of the people of this area. At the same time, we are concerned that building a new power station will only benefit the town's wealthy industrial leaders at the expense of the working class and the poor. You know what I'm talkin' about, you've seen it too! Cities where construction plans place power stations in the backyards of the town's *poorest* citizens, placing their health at ENORMOUS risk, just to save a few precious dollars! Civic leaders turn their backs on the underprivileged precisely because they *are* poor and they don't have *big money* to contribute to election campaigns. BUT NOT HERE! NOT IN OUR TOWN! We will FIGHT THE POWER! Even if there is a need for more electricity, there is NOT a need to overlook the welfare of our citizens! We are organizing to give this group a *voice*. OCC may not have the same financial clout as this city's wealthier citizens, but we still can vote!

Reporter -
Thank you, Reverend. Now we'll speak to Miranda Hutcheson-Wade, the spokesperson for another interested group of citizens, the Lakeside Home Owners Association. Ms.Wade?

(LHA) Lakeside Home Owners Association -
Miranda Hutcheson-Wade, Spokesperson -
Thank you Ms. Jemson, you are too kind. The homeowners I represent all live on small lakes within the nearby counties. We are quite concerned that if a power plant is built, it may be built near us where there is enough water for operating a power station. Homeowners invested here because of the natural beauty and peaceful surroundings. This once-peaceful and natural area is already threatened by increasing traffic and commercial development. In addition, many of the homes on Spring Lake are vacation and retirement homes for their owners. Property values in our community have been increasing slowly and would definitely decline if an eyesore like a power station were to be built nearby. We are not against progress, but if progress means a new power station, we feel that progress should occur somewhere else.

Reporter -
Thank you, Miranda.

We have another spokesperson available to speak to us, Anthony Chen from the Wetland Preservation Society. Go ahead, Mr. Chen.

(WPS) Wetland Preservation Society -
Anthony Chen, Spokesperson -
Wetlands are continually threatened by industrialization. About 150 years ago, 20% of the state was covered by wetlands. Today, that number is less than 3%. About one year ago, a manufacturing plant was constructed along the nearby river. The wastewater dumped into the river by the plant has changed its water temperature enough to cause a decline in several native fish populations. The migratory flyway of Canada geese was also disrupted. In addition to the potential natural damage, this area is an important floodplain for the major area rivers. If developed, surrounding farmland may frequently be flooded. We know that wetlands are inexpensive to build on and therefore, they are often filled in and developed for housing, industry or power stations. But in this case, why don't we just buy electricity from other power stations? Surely this will be much cheaper than the costs associated with building and maintaining a brand-new power plant.

I also want to say something about mercury. Fossil fuel power plants emit mercury, which, as everyone knows, is VERY toxic to the nervous system. When the mercury enters water–like those in wetlands–fish accumulate mercury in their bodies. In Wisconsin today, there are already more than 300 lakes and other bodies of water whose fish are too contaminated with mercury to be eaten by people. When wildlife eat these fish, their offspring have birth defects or are born dead. Why should we build another power plant to poison fish–and the people and wildlife that eat them–even more? I think energy conservation is the answer–the ONLY answer.

Reporter -
Thank you, Mr. Chen. And here we have Randy Adams, author of Holistic Cures for a Sick Planet, from Lifestyles for Sustainable Existence. What issues are you raising?

(LFSE) Lifestyles for Sustainable Existence -
Randy "my other car is a snowboard" Adams, author of *Holistic Cures for a Sick Planet*, Spokesperson -
Like, it's *extraordinary* that of all of the millions of species on this planet, the human race alone is responsible for undoing what took Mother Nature, like, billions of years to assemble. Man, *homo sapiens* spread across this planet like a plague, sucking the energy out of every last energy reserve and leaving behind a wasted landscape that will require another, like, billion years to re-sculpt. You know, we have the technology to stop this process. Man, we don't need any more electricity! In fact, there is no guarantee that another power station will help this situation. Man, this is an opportunity like no other! The whole community needs to step back, evaluate their energy demands, identify the excess in their lives and begin cutting back. In fact, I vote that we should go back to being one with nature, you know, we could do without all these unnecessary luxuries like microwaves and TV's, or even toilets for that matter...

Reporter -
Um, ahem, thank you, Mr. Adams. That is certainly something worth thinking about.

We also have a representative from the Alternative Energy Alliance. Joan Gariboldi is their spokesperson. Ms. Gariboldi?

(AEA) Alternative Energy Alliance -
Joan Gariboldi, Spokesperson -
First of all, I want to point out that we are in favor of economic progress, and with progress, we need more electricity. However, we oppose any solution that does not explore alternative options to the traditional fossil fuel-burning power stations. In 1997, the United States released 1.3 billion tons of carbon dioxide into the atmosphere. The United States should be working on solutions to reduce its emissions and lessen the impact of carbon dioxide on our global climate. If we are to build another power station, then our community needs a cleaner source of power. We hope City Hall will consider solar, wind, or hydroelectric power generation as alternatives.

Reporter -
As you can see, many issues are raised from something as seemingly simple as power outages. The solution doesn't appear to be an easy one.

Now let's hear from Dr. Maya Barr, a research geneticist who has served on several mayoral task forces. Dr. Barr, how have the recent power outages affected your work? Does the mayor have any plans to remedy this situation?

Dr. Barr -

Thank you, Genna. These past few weeks I've been conducting experiments on the growth of cancer cells in field mice. The samples I am working with are very sensitive and need to be regulated at constant temperatures. Because of the brownouts and power outages, my samples have been ruined. It will take months to generate new samples for study. I've tried waiting patiently in the hope that this situation will be resolved soon. Since it doesn't seem like any progress is being made, I've decided to take some action myself and convince city officials to get involved.

Reporter -

What steps have you taken to get involved?

Dr. Barr -

Yesterday, I met with the mayor. She's agreed to appoint a task force of environmental scientists to look into the matter. I understand that this task force will research our electricity needs and recommend a solution to our electricity problems.

Reporter -

Thank you. We have yet to hear from the mayor regarding the appointment of the task force. I'm sure everyone is as eager as I am to hear how this problem will be solved. We will continue to follow the progress of this city's *electrical dilemma* as it unfolds. Back to you, Bob.

Stakeholders and Evidence

 Essential Question: What missing pieces of evidence are needed to support the statements of the stakeholders?

Overview

When making an argument, people often present both evidence and opinion to support their claim. How often do you distinguish between the two when listening to someone making an argument? In this activity, you will critically examine the arguments made by a stakeholder in *Electrical Dilemma*. You will make a distinction between the evidence and the opinions and present your findings to the class.

Procedure

1. As a class, you will make two stakeholder charts based on the *Electrical Dilemma* script. Your teacher will assign you to one character in the script. Complete Step 2 for your character and share your answers with the class.

2. For your character, record the following information for each stakeholder chart.
   - character name and stakeholder group they represent
   - **effects** on that group of building or not building a plant
   - whether the effect is supported by **evidence or opinions**

3. As a class, combine your rows into two completed charts.

Analysis Questions

1. Did any of the people interviewed in *Electrical Dilemma* support their arguments with evidence? If so, which ones?

2. For those people who did not use evidence, how did they try to convince you that they are correct? Were they convincing?

3. Answer the essential question: *What missing pieces of evidence are needed to support the statements of the stakeholders?*

Stakeholders Chart if a fossil fuel power plant IS built

Who are the **stakeholders** that will be affected by this action? (include **character** name)	In what way(s) will they be affected? (Note whether there is **evidence** to support the statement, or if it is an **opinion**)	+ or −	Is this effect the intended goal of the action or is it a side effect?	Has the stakeholder placed himself/herself in this position voluntarily and with appropriate understanding of the risks involved?

Stakeholders chart if a fossil fuel power plant IS NOT built

Who are the stakeholders that will be affected by this action? (include **character** name)	In what way(s) will they be affected?	+ or –	Is this effect the intended goal of the action or is it a side effect?	Has the stakeholder placed himself/herself in this position voluntarily and with appropriate understanding of the risks involved?	How important to YOU are the interests of this stakeholder? 1=very important 2=somewhat important 3=unimportant	If the effect is negative, do YOU feel it is directly offset by greater good elsewhere?

Lesson 2
What is Electricity?

 Driving Question: *What is electricity and how does it work?*

Overview

Your first step as members of the environmental task force is to understand electricity and how it works. This lesson will remind you of the basics of electricity. You will think about the issues surrounding electricity generation and the impacts of using electricity. Without electricity, your life would be very different. Even 50 years ago, people used electricity much less than we do today. You will explore how electricity is generated and how it affects the environment. You will also study how electricity moves from place to place. You will start this lesson by reviewing some electricity concepts. You will then do a lab exercise about electrical circuits to see how electricity moves.

Important Content

- The electricity that we use every day is the result of the movement of electrons in currents.

 **Electricity**

Electricity Summary

 Essential Question: What are three important things to understand about electricity?

Overview

In the previous activity, you were introduced to a community in southeastern Wisconsin that is faced with the problem of how to address the energy demand for a growing population. As populations in cities grow, so does the need to generate more electricity. This need for electricity sometimes results in the building of new power plants. This construction of power plants can create problems such as the ones the southeastern Wisconsin community is facing. Having a basic understanding of electricity is essential to solving these problems.

As you have learned from the previous lesson, one form of energy that is in high demand is electricity. In this activity, you will review how electricity works. You will also review how it was developed and how it affects our everyday lives. In the next lesson, you will explore how electricity can be generated from other sources of energy. You will also study how energy is changed from one form to another.

Read the following passage and answer the questions that follow.

Electricity and Current

Static Charges

All matter is composed of very small particles called atoms. Atoms contain nuclear particles (protons and neutrons) and electrons that swirl around the nucleus. Protons, neutrons, and electrons are very different, each having its own properties. One of these properties is called an electrical charge. Protons have a "positive" (+) charge. Electrons have a "negative" (-) charge. Neutrons have no charge—-they are neutral. The charge of one proton is equal in strength to the charge of one electron. When the number of protons in an atom equals the number of electrons, the atom itself has no overall charge. It is neutral.

There are more than 100 types of atoms, or elements. The atoms of each element have a particular number of protons and electrons. The number of protons is especially important because they define the element. Each has its own particular number of protons. For example, hydrogen, is the simplest element with just one proton and one electron, whereas, oxygen has eight protons and eight electrons. Unlike protons, neutrons are very hard to move. Electrons move (added or subtracted from an atom) fairly easily. When electrons move to or from an atom it changes the total number of electrons in the atom. In this case, the positive and negative charges no longer balance and a charge is formed.

Static electricity is created by the simple rubbing of an object against another object. The rubbing action moves electrons from one object to another. For example, a balloon rubbed quickly against wool will transfer electrons from the wool to the balloon. This movement of electrons away from the wool gives the wool a positive charge. The movement of electrons to the balloon gives the balloon a negative charge. Because "opposites attract," the (negatively charged) balloon will stick to the (positively charged) wool. While opposite charges are attracted to each other, like charges repel. This is why it is also possible for a charged object to make the electrons in a neutral (no charge) object move. For example, if you hold the rubbed (negatively charged) balloon next to a wall, it will cause electrons in the wall to move slightly away from all the electrons in the balloon. This attracts the negative electrons on the balloon to the positive charge on the wall and the balloon will stick to the wall. Some objects are better conductors of electricity than others, which contain material that is easier for electrons to move through. If the neutral object is a good conductor of electricity such as copper, many electrons will move and there will be a strong attraction. If the neutral object is an insulator (not a good conductor of electricity), such as rubber, few electrons will move in it, resulting in a weak attraction.

Current

Walking across a carpet moves electrons from the carpet to your body, giving you extra electrons. Touch a metal doorknob and ZAP! The metal doorknob is a conductor. The electrons move from you to the knob and you get an electric shock.

The movement of electric charges from one place to another because of the difference in charge is called an electric current. When you walk across a carpet, electrons move from the carpet into you. You don't notice it because no current is generated. You are simply adding electrons and building up your charge. When you touch the metal doorknob though, you definitely notice the current when it flows out of you and onto the metal doorknob!

Friction is one way an electrical charge can build up in an object. When there is enough difference in the built-up charge between two objects, electrons will flow. This happens when you walk across a carpet and touch a doorknob. Since the metal doorknob is a conductor, the electrons will move easily away from you into the metal doorknob. This leaves you positively charged and the doorknob negatively charged. All of your extra negative electrons have gone into the doorknob. This difference in charges across the two objects generates a current. Electric current always flows from an object that has a high electrical charge to an object that has a lower electrical charge, from negative to positive. Several factors influence how great a difference in charge there must be before a current will flow. One factor is the composition of each object. Another is the material between the two objects, such as air or water.

A flow of electrons–an electrical current–is a transfer of energy. We usually experience currents of electricity through the wires that pass from power plants to our homes. These wires carry electric current, and we use that current to power appliances in our homes. For example, when this current passes through the filament of a light bulb, the filament lights up. The electrons passing through the thin wire collide with the atoms that make up the wire. Some of the electrons' energy is transferred to the wire's atoms. This causes the atoms to move slightly, so they heat up. The filament gets so hot, the metal wire glows and light is produced. Other appliances use the electrons to make heat, motion, and light.

Analysis Questions

1. What part of an atom is responsible for electric charges and currents?

2. What is an electric current?

3. Answer the essential question: *What are three important things to understand about electricity?*

Circuits

 Essential Question: *What is necessary for a current to move through a battery to a light bulb?*

Overview

Today, you will explore in more detail how electricity moves. Electricity is generated at power plants but how does it get to the places where we use it? It travels through electrical circuits, which allow a current of electrons to flow from one place to another. You can think about this activity in terms of power plants and places where consumers of electricity live. The batteries represent the power plants but how does the electricity get from the power plant to your toaster?

When batteries and light bulbs are connected in various arrangements, some bulbs may light and others may not. You will study electric circuits by observing under which conditions bulbs light brightly, dimly, or not at all.

Materials

1 "D" sized battery

1 small light bulb

1 piece of wire

Safety Concerns

Follow standard safety rules and school safety rules for laboratory activities.

Procedure

1. Obtain one battery and one light bulb from your teacher.

2. Sketch a picture of the battery that indicates the positive (+) and negative (–) end.

3. Sketch a picture of the bulb. Be sure to show (and describe) what's inside the glass bulb.

> **Stop and Think**
>
> If you had one piece of wire, how could you make your light bulb light? Sketch your plan.

4. Connect your equipment in as many ways as you can until the light turns on. Sketch this arrangement.

5. You should be able to find at least four arrangements of the battery, light bulb, and wire that will make the bulb light. Sketch all four arrangements.

Analysis Questions

1. Does it matter which part of the bulb is connected to the positive end of the battery? (The positive end has the bump on it.)

2. List at least two things that all four of your "working" setups have in common.

3. Answer the essential question: *What is necessary for a current to move through a battery to a light bulb?*

Lesson 3
Energy Transformations

 Driving Question: *Where does electricity come from?*

Overview

You know that people need electricity. You know what electricity is. But do you know how we get it? Electricity occurs naturally as lightning, but we do not use that electricity. So where does the electricity we use come from? In this lesson, you will study what energy is and how energy and electricity are related. You will see demonstrations and make observations. You will explore how we use naturally occurring energy to make electricity for our power appliances, lights, and other technology. You will see that when we change energy from those natural forms to electricity, some energy is lost as heat. Finally, you will look at different machines that people use to change energy from one form to another.

Important Content

- Many different energy transformations can lead to useful power generation.

- As energy is transformed, we can identify the kind of energy it is changed into.

Types of Energy

 Essential Questions: How are the six types of energy different from each other? How are they similar?

Overview

In the last lesson, you learned what electricity is and how it moves. Do you know where the electricity you use comes from? There are many different kinds of energy. Electricity is just one kind of energy. We use other forms of energy. For example, we use gasoline to move cars, fireplaces to warm homes, and wind to turn windmills. In this activity, you will brainstorm the different types of energy you use and try to put them into categories. As you think about the different kinds of energy, think about their similarities and differences.

Discussion Notes

1. Brainstorm with your group as many types of energy as you can.

2. Discuss with your class all the types of energy you thought of.

3. After your class discussion, write down the six types of energy and a few examples of each one.

TYPE OF ENERGY	DESCRIPTION AND EXAMPLES

Analysis Questions

1. Which types of energy do you use most often in your daily life?

2. If you listed electricity as the answer to Question 1, do you use the electricity directly, or do you use something that the electricity turns into?

3. Answer the essential questions: *How are the six types of energy different from each other? How are they similar?*

Converting Energy – Part 1

Essential Question: *What energy transformations seem to be most common?*

Overview

In the last activity, you looked at different types of energy. The types of energy you use most often, like electricity, are usually not used directly. Instead, electricity is changed into other types of energy – like heat and light. Even electricity often begins as a different type of energy. It is transformed into electricity so we can move it easily to our homes and businesses. In this activity, you will study transformations of energy. You will be looking at demonstrations of energy transformation. As you observe these energy transformations think about other places in your life where energy transformation might be happening and why it might be useful.

Safety Concerns

Follow standard safety rules and school safety rules for laboratory activities.

Procedure

At each lab station, you will complete an input/output diagram. Follow these steps:

1. Put the station name and number at the top of the diagram as the title.

2. In the center box, write what you are observing.

3. On the left side, write the type of each kind of energy and matter that enter the system you are observing. Distinguish between kinds of energy and phases of matter. Some items may appear in both lists. For example, a burning candle has chemical energy (the burning of the wax) but the wax is also matter.

4. On the right side, write the type of each kind of energy and matter that leave the system you are observing. Some items may be listed in both the matter and energy area because energy can cause matter to change form. Water (matter) with heat (energy) can become steam. Steam is matter but has more energy than liquid water.

Analysis Questions

1. For each energy transformation you saw, list a few other examples of that kind of transformation.

2. For each energy transformation you saw, give a few reasons why it might be a useful transformation.

3. What output is common to every input/output model that you completed?

4. Answer the essential question: *What energy transformations seem to be most common?* Give examples.

Input Output Diagram Example #1

Title and station: **stomping feet**

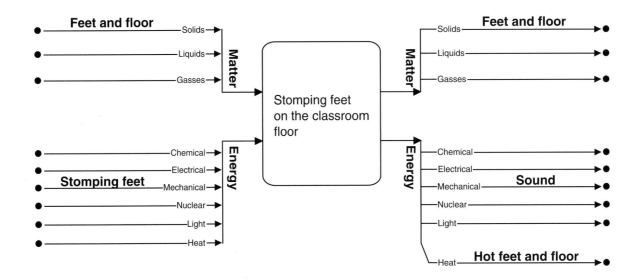

Input Output Diagram Example #2

Title and station: **burning candle**

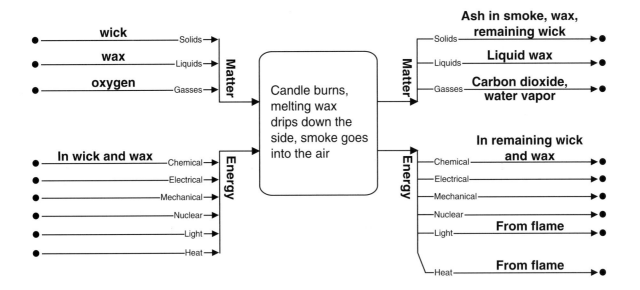

Input Output Diagram

Title and station:

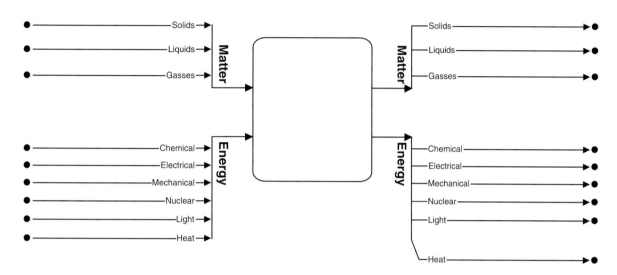

Description:

Input Output Diagram

Title and station:

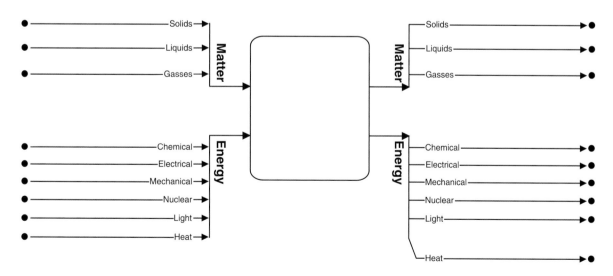

Description:

Input Output Diagram

Title and station:

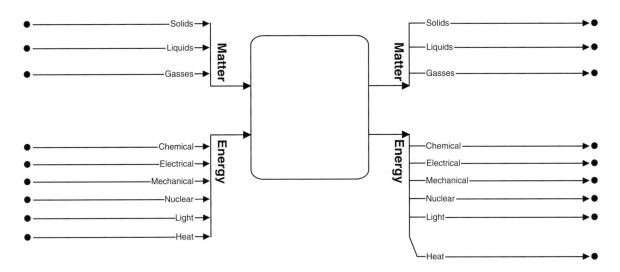

Description:

Input Output Diagram

Title and station:

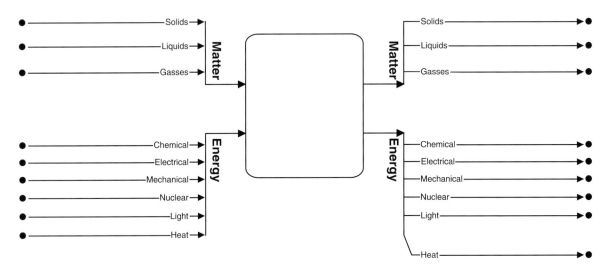

Description:

Input Output Diagram

Title and station:

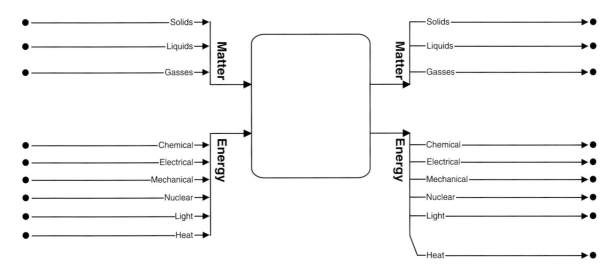

Description:

Input Output Diagram

Title and station:

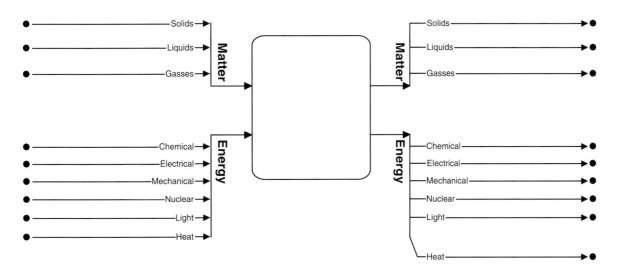

Description:

Converting Energy – Part 2

Essential Questions: *Of the energy transformations you saw today, which one seemed to be the most useful? Why?*

Overview

In this activity, you will look into more energy transformations. These situations are more complicated than the ones you worked on in the last activity. They will require more than one input/output diagram to describe them.

Procedure

At each lab station, do the following:

1. Identify the energy transformations that are occurring. In this activity, each station has at least two transformations.

2. For each transformation, complete an input /output diagram. See the directions in Lesson 3: *Converting Energy – Part 1* for more information.

Safety Concerns

Follow standard safety rules and school safety rules for laboratory activities.

Analysis Questions

Your teacher will assign your group one station to present to the class. For this station, do the following:

1. Identify each energy transformation that occurs. Prepare an input/output diagram to show each transformation.

2. Think of the entire station as one "system," with inputs and outputs. Diagram the entire system on one input/output diagram.

3. Answer the essential questions: *Of the energy transformations you saw today, which one seemed to be the most useful? Why?*

Technology to Transform Energy

Essential Question: *What types of energy transformations are most common in our daily lives?*

Procedure

Complete the chart below by identifying a tool or device humans use to convert one form of energy into another. Identify only tools whose primary purpose is to produce the listed energy. For example, light bulbs take electrical energy and produce heat, but their primary purpose is to produce light. So they should be written in the chart where the electrical row crosses the light column.

From:	To: Chemical	Electrical	Light	Mechanical	Heat
Chemical					
Electrical			Light bulb		
Light					
Mechanical					
Heat					

Analysis Question

1. Answer the essential question: *What types of energy transformations are most common in our daily lives?*

Lesson 4
Large Scale Electricity Generation

Driving Question: What energy transformations are useful on a large scale?

Overview

Many of the energy transformations you studied in Lesson 3 produced electricity. However, not all of them can be used on a large scale to solve energy shortages. In this lesson, you will look closer at energy transformations and put them into categories. You will also think of other energy transformations in your life. You will decide which transformations could be used to generate electricity on a large scale to power entire cities. In the next chapter, you will explore power plants in depth to see how electricity is generated and delivered to your home.

Important Content

- Sources of electricity (other than fossil fuels) are available, but not as widely used. These include hydroelectric power, solar power, power from biomass, nuclear power, and others.

- When determining the best way to generate electricity for a community, it is important to look at the available local resources.

Energy in the World

Essential Question: *Which type of power makes the most sense for your community and for the entire United States? Base your answer on resource availability.*

Overview

You have studied energy transformations and made diagrams of how they work. Now you need to apply that knowledge to generating energy in the real world. People all over the world use their geology and geography to aid them in obtaining energy. The methods for transforming energy that you listed in Lesson 3 require resources from the environment to produce electricity. In this activity, you will read about where those resources come from.

Resources for Generating Electricity

Chemical energy can be found in coal, natural gas, oil, trees, and plants. Any of these fuels can be burned to release their chemical energy. The heat energy released from burning can be transformed into electricity. Coal, natural gas and oil are all types of fossil fuels. They are found mainly in the western and northeastern parts of the U.S. These fuels are also found in large quantities in the Middle East, in Russia, and in parts of South America and Africa. Trees and plants can also be burned for energy. Anywhere there is a forest, there is a source of chemical energy.

Light energy from the Sun is used to generate electricity. Also called solar energy, this type of power is available any time the Sun is shining. The cells used to gather solar energy are called photovoltaic. They are expensive, so they are used where sunlight is most common. Locations with many sunny days, like the southern part of the U.S., are best for harnessing solar energy.

Mechanical energy from falling water and ocean tides can also be used to generate electricity. All that is needed to generate electricity from falling water is a river and a drop in elevation. This power is called hydroelectric. Any of the mountainous states in the U.S. have a high potential for generating electricity from water power. States in the Pacific Northwest are also good candidates. They have a high supply of mountainous resources and many rivers available. Generating power from the oceans' tides is used less frequently. However, its use is increasing as the technology to harness the power of the oceans improves.

Nuclear energy is used in many parts of the world to generate electricity. Nuclear energy is released from the mineral uranium. Uranium is found in Australia, Kazakhstan, Canada, South Africa, Namibia, Brazil, Russia, the U.S., and Uzbekistan. In comparison to other countries on the list, the U.S. mines very little uranium, mainly in the western states. Nuclear power is a clean way to generate electricity, but it also involves risks. Disposal of radioactive waste and the possibility of nuclear accidents make some countries hesitant to use it.

Heat energy is another naturally occurring source of energy that can be transformed into electricity. Heat from the Earth, called geothermal energy, can be used in certain areas of the world to heat buildings or generate electricity. Scientists drill underground to sources of hot air or hot water. This hot water or steam travels to the surface where it can be used for power. These sources of hot water are usually found where Earth's crustal and oceanic plates join together, rub against each other, or slide beneath each other. The countries currently producing the most geothermal energy are the U.S., New Zealand, Italy, Iceland, Mexico, the Philippines, Indonesia, and Japan. Geothermal energy is also used in many other countries. In the U.S., geothermal energy is used in Hawaii, California, Oregon, Idaho, Nevada, New Mexico, and Utah.

These are just some of the ways electricity is generated from natural resources. Scientists are always thinking of new ways to harness Earth's resources to provide power for our growing human population.

Analysis Questions

1. List the natural resources from the reading that can be found in your community or state.

2. Predict how your community or state gets electricity. Put the following list of energy sources in order, with the one used the most first and the least last.

   a. coal and other fossil fuels
   b. nuclear
   c. hydroelectric
   d. solar
   e. wind
   f. biomass
   g. geothermal
   h. tidal

3. Use the same list to predict how the United States gets its electricity.

4. Were your lists different for your community and for the United States? Why?

5. Answer the essential question: *Which type of power makes the most sense for your community and for the entire United States?* Base your answer on resource availability.

Local Power Sources

Essential Questions: *Do the energy resources in the U.S. match up with the way it generates electricity? In Wisconsin? In your own community?*

Overview

You have read about how electricity can be generated from a variety of energy sources. Now it is time to look at what sources are actually used to generate electricity. Your predictions from Lesson 4: *Large Scale Electricity Generation* were based on resource availability and the most commonly used power sources in the U.S. In this activity, you will look at where electricity actually comes from in the U.S, in southeastern Wisconsin, and in your own community. As you look at this information, think about why these types of power are used.

Electricity Generation in the United States

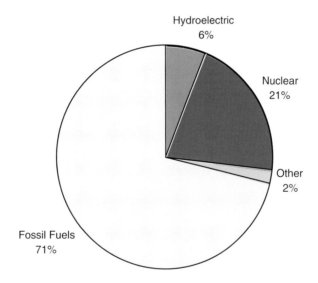

Electricity Generation in the Wisconsin

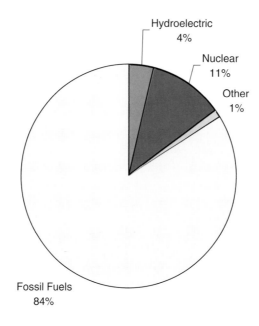

Hydroelectric
4%

Nuclear
11%

Other
1%

Fossil Fuels
84%

Most of the electricity in Wisconsin is generated by burning fossil fuels. However, there are no sources of fossil fuels available in Wisconsin. All of the fossil fuels used must be imported from other locations – usually from the west or the northeast parts of the U.S. Wisconsin is covered in forests and farmlands. There are some large hills, but there are no mountains in the area. Wisconsin is in the northern part of the country, so the days are short in the winter. On average, there are 95 clear, sunny days in Wisconsin each year. This compares to 57 clear days per year in Seattle, and 214 in Phoenix, Arizona. Wisconsin has no geothermal energy sources, and no sources of nuclear fuel.

Analysis Questions

1. Look back at your predictions of electricity generation in the U.S. and your community. Were your predictions correct?

2. Based on the chart and the description of Wisconsin, are you surprised by how the state generates electricity?

3. Answer the essential questions: *Do the energy resources in the U.S. match up with the way it generates electricity? In Wisconsin? In your own community?*

Fossil Fuels

Chapter 2
Fossil Fuels

Connections

As the human population grows, so does the demand for more energy and water resources. In the previous chapter you learned there are many ways to generate electricity. There are also many power sources available with which to do it. By the end of the unit, you will understand the available energy sources used in the U.S., the short and long-term environmental impacts of those energy sources and the tensions power plant companies face when trying to meet the needs of the consumer and the environment. At the end of the unit, you will select the best type of energy generation for a region in the U.S. based on its resources, needs and values.

In the previous chapter, you have learned about a southeastern Wisconsin community's need for more electricity. The most common type of electrical generation in Wisconsin is from burning fossil fuels. Which means to meet the need for more electricity, this community is going to have to build another fossil fuel power plant. To help them determine the location of this new power plant, we need to learn more about how energy is generated from fossil fuels.

In this chapter:

In this chapter, you will explore fossil fuel-burning power plants and the energy transformations that generate electricity. You will take a virtual tour of a power plant to explore the inner workings of electricity generation. You will act as director of a power plant and make decisions about blackouts, transporting coal, and the increasing demand for energy. You will also explore your own energy use. You will see if there are ways you could use less electricity without drastic changes to your lifestyle. This information will help you in later chapters when you will have to make a decision for the residents of Wisconsin. You will have to balance the inputs and outputs of the power plant. Finally, you will determine the most environmentally viable place to build a power plant.

When you're done you'll be able to:

- identify the parts of a power plant, and discuss how energy can be efficiently transformed.

- distinguish between different grades of coal, and explain why the grades of coal are important in the generation of electricity.

- estimate the amount of electricity used by an average family in the U.S.

Lesson 1
What are Fossil Fuels?

Driving Question: *Why are fossil fuels considered to be non-renewable?*

Overview

Most of the world's electricity is generated by burning fossil fuels. Fossil fuels include oil, natural gas, and coal. You will study coal because it is most commonly used for electricity generation in Wisconsin and the U.S. Though there are differences between different fossil fuels, there are also many similarities. You'll read about how coal is formed. You will use your knowledge of energy transformations to study how coal stores so much energy and why it takes so long to develop. You will read about how coal is mined and evaluate the environmental effects of coal mining.

Important Content

- Fossil fuels, including coal, natural gas and oil, are non-renewable resources. Fossil fuels have some different properties but are formed in similar ways.

- Coal is available mainly in the west and northeast of the U.S. The quality of that coal and the way that it is mined depend on local conditions.

- Coal can be found in several different grades of quality. Each grade has specific properties, and higher quality grades are better for use in generating electricity.

Properties of Coal

Essential Question: *What are the major categories of coal, and what are the most observable properties of each?*

Overview

In this activity, you will begin to explore coal. Coal is the energy source that is most commonly used in the U.S. to generate electricity.

Materials

For each group of 4 students
samples of four different types of coal: anthracite, bituminous, lignite, and peat
electronic balance

For each pair of students
glass slide
magnifying glass
100 mL graduated cylinder

Safety Concerns

Follow standard safety rules and school safety rules for laboratory activities.

Procedure

You will test the following five properties for each sample of coal: color, luster, texture, hardness, and density. Construct a data table to record your observations.

Read the descriptions below for each property test before creating a data table.

Color

1. Using the magnifying glass, carefully observe the appearance of each coal sample. Be sure to describe any color patterns or variations that exist.

Luster

2. Luster refers to the shininess of an object. Using the magnifying glass, carefully observe the appearance of each coal sample. Record whether or not it shines.

Texture

3. Texture is the smoothness or roughness of a surface. Feel each sample of coal and record how the sample feels.

Hardness

4. Coal samples vary in hardness based on the amount of moisture they contain. To test this property, gently rub each sample across the glass slide. If the sample leaves a scratch that does not rub away easily, it is harder than glass. If no scratch is present or if it rubs off, the sample is softer than glass. On your data table, enter hardness as harder than or softer than glass.

Density

5. Use the electronic balance to find the mass of one coal sample and record it in the data table.

6. Find the volume of each sample by measuring the amount of water each coal sample displaces. Do this by filling a graduated cylinder halfway with water. Note how much water is in the cylinder. Add the coal piece to the cylinder. Note the new volume. Subtract to find the volume of the coal.

7. Divide the mass by the volume to find the density. Record the density in your data table.

Analysis Questions

1. What similarities did you notice among all the coal samples?

2. What are the major differences among the samples of coal?

3. Answer the essential question: *What are the major categories of coal, and what are the most observable properties of each?*

How Is Coal Formed?

 Essential Question: Why is coal considered a non-renewable resource?

Overview

In the previous lesson – Properties of Coal – you learned that different kinds of coal have different properties. These properties can be used to distinguish between the types of coal and to assess their ability to generate electricity. The coal samples you tested represent the end result of a long process of coal formation. However, have you ever wondered what coal really is and how it is formed? Now that you know about the differences among types of coal, read about what gives each type its different properties.

What Is Coal?

Coal is a rock that burns easily. Coal is made up of at least 50% (by weight) of carbon-based material. The carbon in coal comes from the compacting and hardening of ancient, buried plants. Most coal is fossil (extremely ancient but preserved) peat. **Peat** is a fairly loose, spongy deposit of plant remains from a water-saturated environment, such as a bog or mire. If you look closely at peat, you can see some of the structures of the ancient, rotted plant matter. When dried, peat burns freely. Figure 1 shows a swamp that over many, many years will turn into peat. As generations of swamp plants die, they fall to the ground, then decay, which get buried and become compacted over time. If there is no oxygen present, these plants will become peat.

Figure 1: Swamps that, over time, will form peat and coal.

How Coal Forms

Coal is formed by physical and chemical changes to peat. The process that changes peat involves several steps. It starts with the decay of dead plants. This is followed by their decomposition by bacteria, compaction under layers of soil and other dead plants, and the influence of heat over long periods of time. This process is called **coalification (or carbonization)**, and it's shown in Figure 2.

Coal is a composite of many different carbon and complex hydrocarbon compounds. Hydrocarbons are substances made of hydrogen and carbon. Some of these compounds come from the substances that made up the peat itself. Peat deposits are actually quite varied. Peat may contain everything from preserved plant parts (roots, bark, etc.) to decayed plants. If peat had ever caught fire, it may even be charcoal. Peat deposits usually form in a waterlogged environment where plant debris accumulates, like in peat bogs and peat swamps. In these environments, the accumulation of plant debris is faster than the rate at which bacteria decompose it. The bacterial decay rate is low in bogs and swamps because there's little oxygen. What oxygen is available, it is used up in the process of decomposition. So, the primary decay process in bogs and swamps is anaerobic, or without oxygen. This is a much slower process than aerobic, or with oxygen, decay.

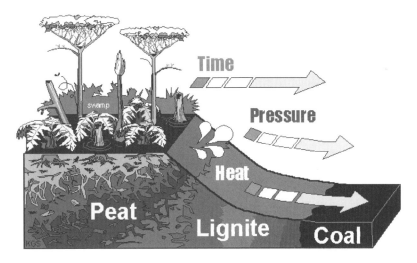

Figure 2: With time, pressure, and heat, peat is transformed into coal.

For peat to become coal, it must be buried by sediment, such as a layer of silty soil. With the passage of enormous amounts of time, there is continued burial and the addition of heat from deep beneath the ground. This causes the hydrocarbon compounds in the deposit to begin breaking down and changing. One change produces methane gas, which is typically expelled from the deposit, as are other elements. As the elements are expelled, the deposit becomes increasingly carbon-rich. This process proceeds in stages from (1) plant debris to (2) peat to (3) coal.

The buried peat is under enormous pressure, as the weight of the overlying soil compacts it. As a result, a lot of water is squeezed out from the peat layer. It is estimated that in the eastern United States 10-20 vertical feet of original peat material produce only 1 vertical foot of bituminous coal. This is because of compaction, loss of water, and the expulsion of elements. However, the peat-to-coal ratio in any deposit is variable. It depends on the original type of peat and the geographical location of the deposit.

Different types of coal

There are several different types of coal as illustrated in Figure 3. In order from least to greatest change from (1) peat, there are: (2) lignite (brown coal), (3) sub-bituminous coal, (4) bituminous coal, (5) anthracite and (6) pure carbon mineral. Pure carbon minerals include graphite or diamond. The last is not considered coal, but is created in the same way as all of the other compounds. Anthracite coal has more carbon and less water than the other types of coal, so it has the greatest amount of energy per unit mass.

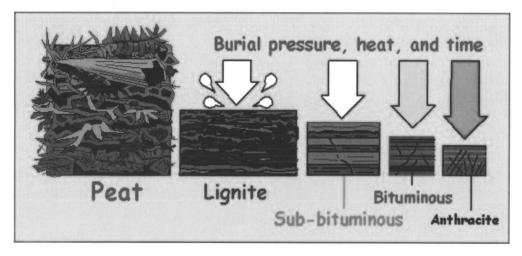

Figure 3: Different types of coal, from peat to anthracite.

Analysis Questions

1. Write a one-paragraph summary explaining the process of coal formation.

2. Which types of coal have the most and the least moisture? What accounts for this variation?

3. Which is the purest type of coal? What makes it "pure?"

4. Answer the essential question: *Why is coal considered a non-renewable resource?*

Methods of Mining Coal

Essential Question: Describe the similarities and differences between surface and underground mining.

Overview

The following article describes how most coal in the U.S. is mined. Read it and answer the analysis questions.

Methods of Mining Coal

Coal mining has been going on for many years in many different ways. Years ago, mining simply involved a pick and a shovel. Men dug the coal and donkeys carried it out of the mines. Modern mining is a highly technological process, using cranes, trucks, and other large machinery.

Coal is usually found underground in large areas called coal seams. A coal seam can be very small or large. Miners have methods to estimate the size of a coal seam before they dig underground to find it. Once the coal seam is located, there are two main ways to mine the coal: surface mining and underground mining.

Surface Mining

If a coal seam is not very deep, surface mining techniques are used. First, the overburden (topsoil and rock that lies on top of the coal) is removed. The exposed coal is dug out of the mine with draglines, front loaders, backhoes and trucks. There are three main types of surface mining. They are strip mining, open pit mining, and mountaintop removal mining.

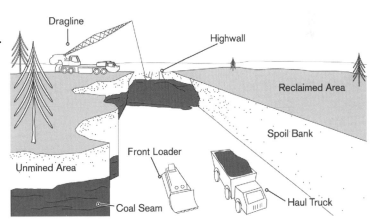

Surface Mine

Strip mining is mining in motion. Following the path of a coal seam, miners remove the overburden and pile it next to the mine. When one section of the coal seam is mined, they move further along the seam, removing new overburden and extracting more coal. This pattern of moving large amounts of soil and removing coal can destroy large sections of

countryside. However, as the mine moves, the overburden can be returned to the mine. This returns the landscape back close to its original state. The piles of overburden that accumulate alongside the mine must be carefully monitored. They are susceptible to slides or movement due to settling and heavy rain. Aside from this risk, strip mining is a very safe mining technique. It is favorable in many areas if the coal seams are close enough to the surface.

Open pit mining is quite similar to strip mining. There are two main differences. Pit mines are stationary because the coal seams they are built to extract are usually larger and deeper. Because there is more coal in one area, the mine does not have to move. This leads to the second difference. Pit mines are often in operation for long periods of time. Pit mines might start out quite small, but as the pit gets deeper, it also gets wider. They can eventually cover several square kilometers.

In *Mountaintop removal*, the top of a mountain is removed to get at the coal that lies within it. The first step in this type of removal is removing all the topsoil and vegetation from the mountaintop. The upper 800 to 1000 feet of the mountain are then blasted away with dynamite. The topsoil and blast debris, called overburden, are dumped in a valley at the foot of the mountain. Mining is done by a machine called a dragline. The dragline scoops out the center of the mountain and, with it, its coal. A dragline is 22 stories tall. The bucket it uses to dig the coal out of the body of the mountain is large enough to hold 24 small cars. The overburden from the digging process is also dumped into valleys surrounding the mountain. Mountaintop removal is probably the most destructive form of surface mining. Unfortunately, it is also a method that is becoming more widespread, especially in Appalachia.

All three types of surface mining cause changes to the environment. The first and most obvious change is in the immediate area around the mine. Vegetation is eliminated and small hills and valleys are often altered. Valleys and streams can be filled with overburden, permanently changing the soil and geography of a region. In addition, the underground water flow and aquifer system can be destroyed by deep pits or strip mines. This alteration in the water system can affect the quality and quantity of local drinking water.

Mining companies can take steps to make fewer impacts on the land and water. They are regulated by reclamation laws, which require them to return much of the land back to its original condition. This process sometimes restores parts of the landscape. However, there are risks associated with mining operations beyond appearance. These include acidification of soil, sulfur contamination from leftover high-sulfur coal, and distribution of metals throughout the soil. These impacts can damage the environment even if the dredged up earth is returned to its previous appearance.

Underground Mining

The second major method of mining coal is underground mining. This method is used when a coal seam is too far underground to reach with surface methods. Underground mining is more dangerous and complex than surface mining. It is also more expensive. To mine coal underground, tunnels are dug to hold the people and machinery who extract the coal. The tunnels must be safe for workers, so the structure of the mine is very important. This concern about mine structure has led to two methods of underground mining. They are room & pillar mining and longwall mining.

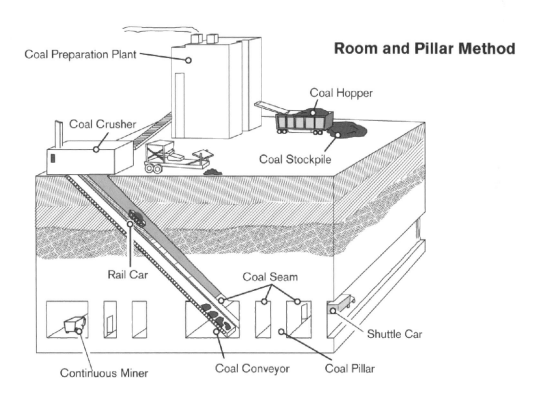

Room & pillar mining refers to mines where parts of the coal seam are left in place to support the ceiling of the mine. Miners leave pillars of coal standing in each tunnel and coal is taken out around the pillars. Wooden or metallic roof beams are installed for extra support. Mechanical drills are used to cut away the coal. Small bulldozers scoop the coal up and transport it to conveyor belts that carry it to the surface. Machines do most of the work, but men must stay underground for long hours to control the machinery. Room and pillar mining can also be assisted by high pressure water sprayers. These sprayers break up the coal and wash it away in streams. The water cuts down on the amount of dust and ash generated by drilling. It is often referred to as "hydraulic mining."

Longwall mining is used when coal seams are at great depths under the surface. Longwall mining uses fewer workers to operate the machinery. Only one large cutter is in the mine at a time. The rotating steel-tooth cutter runs through the coal seam, tearing the coal from the walls. The coal falls onto a conveyor belt, and is carried to the surface. A hydraulic system keeps the roof of the mine from collapsing. However, some of the mine might be allowed to collapse once mining operations are complete in that section of the mine.

Restoring the environment (reclamation) of underground mines is difficult and poses some risks to the environment. Digging deep under the ground can disturb underground water flows. This can affect water supplies and wells in the area. Collapses of underground mines can also cause depressions in the ground at the surface. These depressions can be small or large, depending on the size of the mine.

Analysis Questions

1. What is overburden?

2. If a coal seam is deep underground, what type of mining will be used? Why?

3. Which type of coal mine do you think has the least damaging effect on the environment? Explain your answer.

4. Answer the essential question: *Describe the similarities and differences between surface and underground mining.*

What are Fossil Fuels?

Essential Question: *Why are coal, oil, and natural gas considered to be similar types of fuel?*

Overview

Read the following article about the origin of petroleum.

Types of Fossil Fuels

Why are the three major forms of fuel – coal, oil, and natural gas – called fossil fuels? A fossil is the preserved remains of an organism (a living thing) that died many thousands or millions of years ago. Fossil fuels formed from the remains of long-dead organisms whose organic matter was transformed into a substance we now use as fuel.

During the Carboniferous period, between 360 and 286 million years ago, the world was covered in lush, moist forests. Over the millions of years that have passed since, pressure, heat, decay, and time changed the carbon in these dead plants into peat, and then into coal.

The Carboniferous period was named for the carbon-based resources it produced. It was also a time when great oceans and huge inland seas covered large parts of the planet. Over millions of years, the algae (tiny, single-celled plants) and protozoans (microscopic animals) in these waters died. Their remains were transformed into another type of fossil fuel – petroleum.

Fossil Fuels

Fossil fuels other than coal are formed from the burial and compacting of microscopic algae, bacteria, and protozoans. Two types of fossil fuels have formed this way: oil and natural gas. Most oil and natural gas deposits formed in what were once marine environments. Countless dead organisms sank to the bottom of the sea. They became trapped or covered in sediment and decayed in an anaerobic (without oxygen) environment. Under the influence of pressure, decay, heat, time, and anaerobic conditions, the remains of huge numbers of marine organisms became transformed into fossil fuels. This transformation occurred after a long series of complex chemical reactions changed the organic matter into hydrocarbons, compounds consisting primarily of carbon and hydrogen.

Oil

The organic remains on the sea floor accumulated in layers up to 1000 meters thick. They were under a great deal of pressure from the overlying ocean water, accumulated organic matter, and sediment. Pressure and slow decay heated up the organic material to a temperature between 150° and 350°F. At these temperatures, the organic material became liquid and formed into droplets. These droplets became trapped in the surrounding clay sediment. Over time, it compacted into shale rock. The shale is called "source rock." As more pressure was applied, the rock hardened. The oil droplets were squeezed out of the shale and into more porous rock nearby, like sandstone or limestone. The oil accumulated in the pores of these "reservoir rocks." If there is a barrier around the source rock that prevents the oil from leaking out, the oil becomes concentrated. This barrier is called a trap. It can form due to warping of the surrounding rock or by the presence of a layer that oil cannot penetrate. Today, oil wells are sunk into these reservoirs of oil.

Natural Gas

Natural gas can be found in association with other fossil fuels, such as oil and coal. Oil is formed when the temperature is between 150° and 350°F. Natural gas is formed if the temperature reaches over 350°F but does not exceed 500°F. As a result of such high temperature, some of the organic compounds that comprise oil or coal are heated until they become a gas. The first gas to form is methane (CH_4). Methane gas is lighter than liquid oil or solid coal, so the gas rises and accumulates above the oil. Reservoirs of natural gas, similar to oil, must also be surrounded by impermeable rock. If not trapped by impermeable rock the gas would escape.

Natural gas is odorless and colorless. It usually consists of about 85% methane and 15% ethane. These two compounds are types of hydrocarbons called alkanes. Alkanes consist of saturated chains of hydrogen and carbon. These are chains that contain the maximum possible number of hydrogen atoms. Members of the alkane family include methane (CH_4), ethane (C_2H_6), propane (C_3H_8), and octane (C_8H_{18}). Some of these alkanes may be familiar to you. Propane is a fuel used to heat homes or is sold in cans for camping stoves (LPG, or liquid propane gas). Octane is a component of gasoline, a refined product made from liquid petroleum, or crude oil.

Tar Sands

Oil that is too thick to flow into porous rock is called *oil tar*. This thick, viscous oil acts like a glue that holds together the grains of rock in which it is found, usually sandstone. Mining and refining oil tars used to be very difficult and expensive. However, over the last few years, it has become more affordable. Not all tar sands are mined. Some are extracted as a liquid. The largest occurrence of tar sands is in Alberta, Canada. The region has about 5000 square kilometers (1900 square miles) of tar sands in a layer about 60 meters (200 feet) thick. Tar sands may play a major role in the future energy balance due to their abundance and improvements in mining techniques.

Oil Shale

A very fine-grained type of shale rock, called oil shale, is rich in an oily organic material called *kerogen*. If it's heated, kerogen breaks down into both liquid and gaseous hydrocarbons similar to oil. Large deposits of oil shale exist in the U.S. (mainly in Colorado, Utah, and Wyoming) and Australia. However, the cost of extracting and refining makes use of this fuel impractical at this time.

Reserves and Consumption

The U.S. Energy Information Agency (EIA) reports the following world supply of petroleum:

      Crude oil: 1018.7 billion barrels

      Natural gas: 5457.1 trillion cubic feet

The agency also reports and forecasted the following human consumption of these fuels:

      Crude oil products: 2002: 77 million barrels per day; 2025: 119 million barrels per day.

      Natural gas: 2002: 88 trillion cubic feet per year; 2024: 176 trillion cubic feet per year.

Analysis Questions

1. What conditions had to exist for petroleum to form? Diagram the conditions that led from the deposition of organic matter to the formation of oil and natural gas.

2. In what type of material does petroleum form? Where does it "migrate" and why?

3. How does natural gas form from petroleum deposits?

4. What is a hydrocarbon? What property makes it especially useful as a fuel?

5. Petroleum, which formed in a marine environment, is now often found in desert regions (Saudi Arabia, for example). What do you think accounts for this?

6. Explain why fossil fuels, including petroleum, are called non-renewable. About how long will our petroleum resources last according to estimates of future consumption?

7. Answer the essential question: *Why are coal, oil, and natural gas considered to be similar types of fuel?*

Lesson 2
Stored Energy

Driving Question: *How can stored energy be transformed into heat?*

Overview

Coal is important to us because it is a form of stored chemical energy. Other fossil fuels, such as oil and natural gas, also have stored energy. In this lesson, you will conduct an experiment to look at the amount of stored energy in a different kind of fuel, the food we eat. You will learn how stored energy is measured. You will develop ideas about how much energy is lost when stored energy is transformed into a useful form. You will see similarities between the amounts of stored energy in food and the grades of coal you learned about in Lesson 1. Finally, you will look at the concept of energy efficiency and determine if there are ways to get more energy out of the fuels we burn.

Important Content

- There are many different energy transformations that might lead to useful power generation.

- As energy is transformed, we can identify the kind of energy it is changed into. In almost all cases, some energy is transformed into heat.

Stored Energy in a Peanut

Essential Question: Explain the evidence that peanuts contain energy.

Overview

Since it is difficult to actually build a power plant within your classroom, you are going to model how a power plant works. You will demonstrate energy transformation using something more common – peanuts. By burning peanuts, you will see the amount of energy that is contained inside them. You will see that burning peanuts is also a transformation of energy.

If you burn a peanut, it will give off energy in the form of heat and light. To measure the amount of heat given off, we will use the heat energy from the peanut to heat a container of water. By measuring the temperature change of the water, we can calculate the amount of heat given off by the peanut. The following formula measures the amount of heat.

Mass of water (grams) x temperature change (˚C) = Calories in the peanut (cal)

The calories that you see on food labels are actually kilocalories, or 1000 scientific calories.

Materials

Follow your teacher's instructions for assembling and using a calorimeter.

Safety Concerns

Follow standard safety rules and school safety rules for laboratory activities.

Procedure

1. Record the mass of the peanut in grams in your notebook.

2. Carefully insert the pin through the peanut. (If the peanut falls apart, use another one.)

3. Fill the calorimeter with 100 mL of water.

4. Just before burning the peanut, record the temperature of the water.

5. Light the peanut. Once it begins to burn, slide it under the can and let it burn completely.

6. As soon as it stops burning, stir the water once and record its temperature in your notebook. Leave the apparatus at your desk when finished. **Do not touch the can after you record the temperature!**

7. Repeat the above procedure with two more peanuts.

Data Processing

1. 1 mL of water has a mass of 1 gram. Record the number of grams of water used in your calorimeter.

2. Calculate the temperature change of the water by subtracting the starting temperature from the ending temperature.

3. The number of calories used to raise the temperature is the temperature change multiplied by the mass of the water. Calculate the number of kilocalories used to raise the temperature of the water.

4. Calculate the number of kilocalories per gram in your peanut.

5. Calculate the average number of kilocalories per gram in your peanuts.

Analysis Questions

1. Do you think the number you calculated for the amount of energy in a peanut is lower or higher than the actual value? Explain.

2. Complete an input/output diagram for this energy transformation.

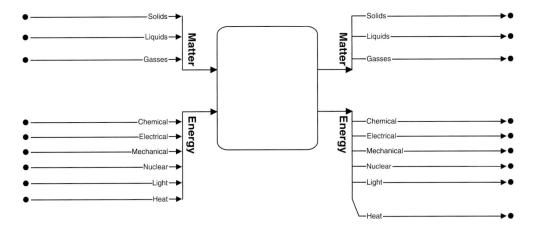

3. Why do you think you were instructed to repeat the above procedure three times?

4. Answer the essential question: *Explain the evidence that peanuts contain energy.*

Releasing Stored Energy

Essential Question: *Does the type of material burned make a difference in the amount of energy that is released?*

Overview

You observed in *Stored Energy in a Peanut* that peanuts contain stored energy. Burning the peanut releases energy, as shown by the heating of the water in the can. In today's activity, you will quantify the number of calories in some other foods and compare their stored energy. In so doing, you will be able to correlate the stored and released energy in food with the information you learned about coal.

Safety Concerns

Follow standard safety rules and school safety rules for laboratory activities.

Procedure

1. Gather the calorimeter you used in the previous lesson and three other food items your teacher will provide.

2. Construct a data table similar to the one below.

Food Item	Mass of food item (g)	Temperature of water before burning ($^{\circ}$C)	Temperature of water after burning ($^{\circ}$C)	Calories

3. Record the mass of the food item in grams in your notebook.

4. Carefully insert the pin through the food item.

5. Fill the calorimeter with 100 mL of water.

6. Just before burning the food item, record the temperature of the water.

7. Light the food item. Once it begins to burn, slide it under the can and let it burn completely.

8. As soon as it stops burning, stir the water once and record its temperature in your notebook. Leave the apparatus at your desk when finished. **Do not touch the can after you record the temperature!**

9. Repeat the procedure with different food items. Change the water after each burn.

10. Use the method explained in *Stored Energy in a Peanut* to help calculate the calories in each of the food items.

Analysis Questions

1. Did these materials all burn in the same way? Explain any differences you observed.

2. Which material has the most stored energy? What evidence do you have for this?

3. Rank the materials in order from least amount of stored energy to the highest amount of stored energy.

4. Most power plants burn coal to generate electricity. Today, you burned food to heat water, and you saw that different foods give off different amounts of energy. Based on what you observed today, which type of food would be the best kind to use in a power plant? Why?

5. Answer the essential question: *Does the type of material burned make a difference in the amount of energy that is released?*

Improving Efficiency

Essential Question: *How would you improve the design of the calorimeter so that you could measure all of the heat released by a burning food source?*

Overview

In the previous two activities, you used water to measure the amount of heat energy given off when a food sample is burned. Some heat from the burning material radiated away from the water into the air, and not all of the food was burned. Other factors also affected the accuracy of your results. The calorimeter you created is not as **efficient** as you might have thought. It does not capture and use the maximum amount of energy produced. There are several factors that affect the efficiency of any fuel-burning apparatus (from a calorimeter to a power plant). Among them are:

*   not all of the fuel (in this case, the food) is thoroughly burned.

*   different fuels give off different amounts of heat (energy) when they are burned. Burning a fuel that does not give off the maximum amount of heat (relative to the amount of fuel burned) is a form of inefficiency. For example, if you burn 10 pounds of wet twigs in a wood stove, you'd get less heat (per pound of wood) than if you burned a 10-pound dry log. The log is therefore a more efficient fuel.

*   some of the heat (energy) generated by the burning of any fuel is lost to the environment. This, too, is a type of inefficiency.

How, then, would you increase the **efficiency** of the calorimeter you used? Your task today is to design the most efficient calorimeter possible. What would you change in the calorimeter design to increase its efficiency? In your design, include improved efficiency in at least two of the above three areas to eliminate or decrease energy loss.

Analysis Questions

1. What was the easiest source of energy loss to remedy? How did your design limit this loss of energy?

2. What, if any, source of energy inefficiency were you unable to eliminate or reduce? Why?

3. Answer the essential question: *How would you improve the design of the calorimeter so that you could measure all of the heat released by a burning food source?* Complete answers should include a diagram with labels as well as a written procedure.

4. How do the improvements you made to the calorimeter relate to the efficiency of power plants? How do you think efficiency at coal-burning power plants might be improved?

Lesson 3
Power Plants

Driving Question: How is energy transformed in a power plant?

Overview

In the last lesson, you burned food to release the stored energy inside. This is very similar to how energy is released from coal and other fossil fuels. In Lesson 3, you will look at how power plants harness energy as electricity and send that electricity to homes and businesses. You will also learn about the different components that make up a power plant by taking a virtual tour. In later chapters, you will use your knowledge of power plants to decide where to build one in Wisconsin to support the population expansion there. Keep in mind the resources needed to generate power and the effects a power plant might have on the environment.

Important Content

- Fossil-fuel power plants use combustion to heat water into steam, which turns a turbine. This turbine generates electricity.

- Power plants require large amounts of water to generate steam, and for cooling. Power plants also require road and rail access, and a location in an appropriate geographic area.

- Each part of the power plant – the boiler, stack, turbine, cooling tower, and water system – involves different energy transformations.

Virtual Tour

Essential Question: _How does a coal power plant work?_

Materials

Computers

Procedure

1. Open the Coal Power Plant virtual tour according to your teacher's instructions.

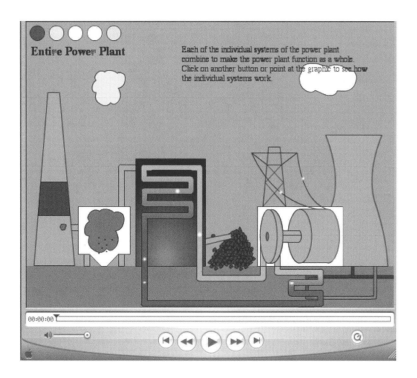

2. Move your mouse over the colored buttons in the upper left corner of the screen to see the power plant in action.

3. Navigate through each system. Pass your mouse over the colored buttons to read details about what is happening in the coal power plant. Answer the analysis questions as you go.

Analysis Questions

1. Label "Boiler," "Precipitator," "Stack," "Generator," "Transmission System," and "Cooling System" on the drawing below.

2. What happens to coal before it is burned?

3. Name two gases and two solid byproducts (also called pollutants or emissions) mentioned in the "pollution control measures" section.

4. What spins the turbine?

5. Write one paragraph (4-5 sentences) to answer the essential question: *How does a coal power plant work?*

Basics of Coal Plants

Essential Question: What are the products of a coal power plant?

Overview

Read the following summary of how a power plant works and how electricity is measured. Answer the analysis questions.

Basics of Coal Power Plants

Coal in the Power Plant
Coal begins its journey through a power plant in the storage yards. Power plants keep tons of coal in storage near the plant, ready for use when the power is needed. When more electricity needs to be generated, coal moves from storage onto a conveyor belt. The conveyor belt takes the coal into a boiler. In the boiler, coal is burned, turning the chemical energy stored in the coal into heat energy. This heat energy is used to boil water and turn it into steam.

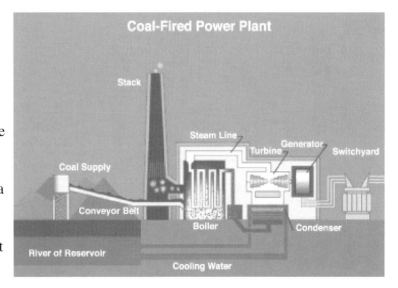

Water in the Power Plant
The steam moves through a series of pipes where it is pressurized and heated further. In the next stage, the kinetic energy in the moving steam is converted to mechanical energy as it spins a turbine. As this fan-shaped turbine spins around large magnets, it creates an electric current. This electric current passes through wires to homes and businesses.

Products
This process leaves several waste products, which must be reused or disposed. The first waste product is coal ash. This is the leftover ash from the burning of coal. There are also large amounts of gases, like carbon dioxide, which are released through the stack or collected for proper disposal. Heat energy still remains in the steam that is left after the turbine spins. This steam is either released from the power plant, or cooled and recycled through the plant. In the plant, it is heated into steam again and continues to spin the turbine.

The amount of electricity that leaves a power plant is measured in watts, kilowatts, or megawatts. Sometimes the demand for electricity is also measured in megawatt hours or kilowatt hours.

What's a Watt?

You have probably seen listings on electrical products that explain how many watts of electricity they use. For example, every light bulb is labeled with 60 watts, 120 watts, etc. This number shows the amount of electricity used by that light bulb. A 60-watt bulb uses half as much electricity as a 120-watt bulb. If you plug in both types of bulb, you can see that 120-watt bulbs put out more light than 60-watt bulbs. Other appliances also list the number of watts they use, from a 180-watt television, to a 1000-watt coffee maker, to a 24,000-watt electric stove. Watts, kilowatts and megawatts are all measures of the same thing. One megawatt equals 1000 kilowatts, and 1 kilowatt equals 1000 watts. (These prefixes, mega- and kilo-, work the same way throughout the metric system. For example, one kilometer is 1000 meters.) These numbers tell how many watts each appliance uses when they are running. An electric bill, however, lists electricity used in kilowatt-hours. A kilowatt-hour is an amount of electricity used over a period of time. For example, a 60-watt bulb left on for one hour would consume 60 watt-hours of electricity. A 24-kilowatt electric stove used to cook a turkey for four hours would use 96 kilowatt-hours (kWh) of electricity.

Analysis Questions

1. What type of energy (mechanical, heat, light or chemical) is stored in coal?

2. List three products of a coal power plant, besides electricity.

3. If a 1000-watt coffee maker runs for four hours, how many kilowatt-hours of electricity will be used?

4. Answer the essential question: *What are the products of a coal power plant?*

Power Plant Inputs and Outputs

 Essential Question: What are all the inputs and outputs of a coal power plant?

Overview

In this lesson, you will use input/output diagrams to explain how a power plant works.

Procedure

Open the Coal Power Plant virtual tour according to your teacher's instructions.

Close the large diagram and open the Systems menu.

For each of the four systems, complete an input-output diagram. Be sure to include both energy and materials on the input and output sides. Refer to Chapter 1, Lesson 3:*Converting Energy Part 1* if you don't remember how to do the diagrams.

Look at the diagrams you drew. Combine them into one diagram that includes all the inputs and outputs for the power plant.

Analysis Questions

1. The inputs you listed will have to be available at a power plant site or they will have to be brought in. All of the outputs will have to be disposed of at the power plant site or they will have to be transported away. How does this affect a location for a power plant in Wisconsin?

2. Answer the essential question: *What are all the inputs and outputs of a coal power plant?*

Sun to Electricity

? **_Essential Question:_** _How many energy transformations occur between the Sun and the electricity that powers light bulbs in our homes?_

Overview

We studied the natural processes that occur over millions of years to convert peat into coal. We learned that temperature and the accumulation of sediment and silt are important factors in coal formation. We also learned that coal can be categorized into different rankings depending on its purity and moisture content. Once coal is formed, there are more stages that occur before it is mined and used in a power plant. In this activity, you will be creating a flow chart. It will explain how the Sun is converted into electricity by a coal-burning power plant.

Procedure

1. Beginning with the Sun, write out the steps that occur in the coal-formation process.

2. Once coal is formed, continue adding steps to your description until electricity is generated.

3. Use arrows to connect the various steps. Write a brief description next to each step so that the concept is clear.

4. Be prepared to share your list and descriptions with the class.

Analysis Questions

1. Answer the essential question: _How many energy transformations occur between the Sun and the electricity that powers light bulbs in our homes?_

2. Draw another flow chart with fewer steps. Show the process of transforming energy from the Sun to the energy in a steak dinner.

Lesson 4

Operating a Power Plant

 Driving Question: What kinds of decisions do power plant operators need to make?

Overview

Operating a power plant requires you to make important decisions every day. These decisions can range anywhere from judging the community's daily demand for electricity, estimating the availability of fossil fuels, and addressing the plant's environmental impacts. In this lesson, you will study these issues, using a computer model to simulate managing a power plant. You will have to meet the electricity demand of consumers in your area as needs change with the seasons. The computer model will show you how complex these decisions can become. In the next chapter, you will learn more about the environmental effects of running a power plant. You will use this information in your final decision on where to place a power plant in southeastern Wisconsin.

Important Content

- There are many issues surrounding power generation, including cost, land-use changes, efficiency considerations, sustainability for different environments, and byproducts generated.

- Almost everything we do requires electricity. Our lives and work are severely interrupted by brownouts and blackouts.

Operating a Power Plant

Essential Question: *Describe what the director of a power plant would need to do to prepare for increasing the amount of electricity generated at the plant.*

Overview

Imagine you are the Director of Operations for a coal-burning power plant. You are in charge of the plant's day-to-day operations and maintenance. You are responsible for making sure that hundreds of thousands of people have uninterrupted electricity. You need to ensure that the power plant has enough coal in reserve. You are also responsible for keeping the emissions of gases (and other hazardous wastes) from exceeding limits set by pollution regulations. It sounds like a big responsibility, doesn't it? Your goal is to meet the demand for electricity without violating emission standards. Are you ready?

Materials

Coal Power Plant Model
File Name: Coal Power Plant Model
File Type: application program

Procedure

1. Open the Coal Power Plant model by double clicking on it. You will see a screen with two options. Choose "Single Emission Plant."

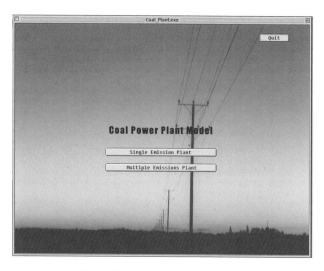

Figure 4: The Coal Power Plant Model. For this activity, choose the "Single Emission Model".

2. This interactive model allows you to adjust the amount of coal you transport from the coal mine to your power plant. You can also adjust the amount of coal you burn to generate electricity.

3. Click on the Start button to start the model.

4. Use the arrows under "Coal Burning Rate" and "Coal Transportation Rate" to explore the model.

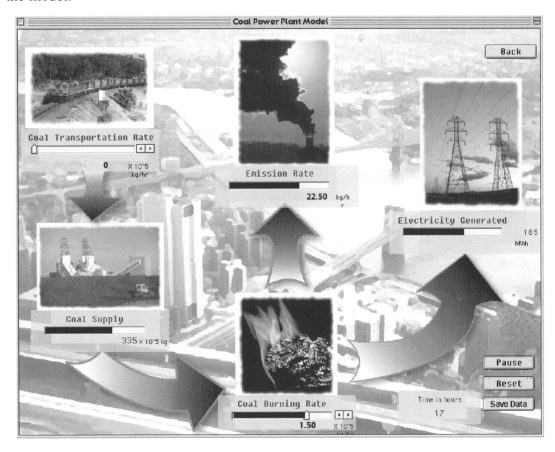

Analysis Questions

1. Describe in one sentence the relationship between the coal-burning rate and electricity generation. In another sentence, describe the relationship between the coal-burning rate and emissions.

2. Describe in a few sentences the relationship between the coal-burning rate and coal supply.

3. Use the model to complete the first three columns of the following chart.

TRIAL	Coal-Burning Rate	Electricity Generated	Emissions	Coal Needed for 10-day Supply	Coal Transportation Rate Needed
1	1.00×10^5 kg/hr				
2		151 MWh			
3	2.00×10^5 kg/hr				

**Note: To run each trial in the chart, click on the Reset button. Then adjust the rates and click Start to see the values for the other columns.

As the director of the power plant, you are responsible for keeping a supply of coal in reserve. If the coal runs out, you can not generate any power. To ensure that you will not run out, you should keep a 10-day supply at the power plant at all times. Calculate how much coal you would need to keep at the plant for each trial in the table above.

To calculate a 10-day supply, use this formula:

coal burning rate x number of hours in a day x 10 days = 10-day supply

Adjust your coal transportation rate for each trial so that you maintain a 10-day supply. Record your answers in the chart above.

4. Answer the essential question: *Describe what the director of a power plant would need to do to prepare for increasing the amount of electricity generated at the plant.*

Demand in Different Seasons

Essential Question: *In your opinion, is it better to violate emissions standards or to leave people without electricity?*

Overview

Now that you know how the Coal Power Plant model works, you will look at some real-life situations. Demand for electricity changes at different times of the year. Air conditioning is one of the major reasons for this. We see energy use peaking at times when temperatures are high. Today, you will see that there is more to consider than simply meeting the demand for electricity. You will need to maintain a supply of coal and keep the plant's harmful emissions below a certain level. State and federal governments restrict the harmful emissions that power plants can release into the environment. You will learn more about these harmful emissions in the next chapter. For today, think about how emissions might change the decisions you make as a power plant director.

Materials

Coal Power Plant Model
File Name: Coal Power Plant Model
File Type: application program

Procedure

Open the Coal Power Plant model by double clicking on it. You will see a screen with two options. Choose "Single Emission Plant."

Test your skills as a Director

There are several rules you must follow in operating this power plant.

1. You must maintain at least a 10-day supply of coal.

2. You must keep harmful emissions at or below 23.4 kg/hour. If you do not, you will pay a severe penalty to the state's Energy Facility Council.

3. You need to maintain a 10% production buffer above the demand for electricity. This will prevent customers from experiencing blackouts.

4. Record required information in the table on the next page.

Situation #1: Winter

The average demand for electricity during winter months is 150 MWh (megawatt hours). Maintain production at your power plant at least 10% above the demand without violating emission standards.

Situation #2: Summer

The average demand for electricity during the summer months is 160 MWh. Maintain production at your power plant at least 10% above the demand without violating emission standards.

Situation #3: Heat Wave

During summer months, the region often experiences a heat wave with temperatures well above normal. When this happens, the demand for electricity averages 200 MWh. Maintain production at your power plant at least 10% above the demand without violating emission standards.

Situation	Situation #1 Winter	Situation #2 Summer	Situation #3 Heat Wave
Electricity Demand			
Electricity Generated (10% above demand)			
Coal Burning Rate			
Coal Supply Needed (10-day supply)			
Transportation Rate (to mainain 10-day supply)			
Harmful Emissions			

Analysis Questions

1. Did you ever violate the emission standards? If so, when?

2. What is the maximum amount of electricity your power plant can produce without violating emission standards?

3. Suppose you don't want to pay the high penalty for violating emissions. What are the consequences for not meeting the electricity demand, particularly during a summer heat wave?

4. Answer the essential question: *In your opinion, is it better to violate emissions standards or to leave people without electricity?* List the benefits and costs for both options.

Lesson 5
Improving Power Plant Efficiency

Driving Question: How can we get the most energy out of the power plants we build?

Overview

This lesson examines ways that coal-burning power plants can be made more efficient. First, you will graph the efficiencies of power plants in the past to see how technology has affected this industry. You will then use your input–output diagrams from earlier in the chapter to identify places in the system where energy is lost. Finally, you will read about scientific developments that make coal-burning power plants more efficient. These new technologies may help us reduce the number of power plants we need to build. Efficiency can increase if our current and future power plants all adopt these new technologies.

Some of the technologies you will read about are already being used. Others are still under development. Their goal is the same – to increase the amount of useful energy produced by burning coal and to reduce the amount of energy wasted. Many of these technologies also help reduce power plant emissions. You will read more about this in the next chapter.

Important Content

*   Coal plants can be made more efficient and less polluting by changing the way coal and air interact in the boiler, or by using a combination of fossil fuels in power plants.

Efficiency Over Time

Essential Question: What has been the efficiency trend over time for coal-burning power plants?

Overview

It looks like the only solution for the community in Wisconsin is to build a new power plant. However, there are other possible solutions. The demand for electricity could be reduced if consumers changed their behavior. Also, improvements could be made in the existing power plants to make them more energy efficient.

Earlier in this chapter, you simulated the first stage of electricity generation by heating water. The peanut and other foods represent the source of energy in a power plant, coal. After measuring the temperature change of the water, you were able to calculate the calories found in each food. As you know, your calorimeter was not perfect. The design allowed a lot of heat to escape and energy was lost. Power plants try to minimize the amount of heat lost during combustion, but a high percentage of energy does escape. Energy transformations are always inefficient to some degree. The data table below indicates the efficiency of the average coal-burning power plant over the last 100 years.

Procedure

1. Make a graph of the data. Put the year on the *x*-axis and the percent efficiency on the *y*-axis.

Typical Coal Power Plant Efficiency

Year	% Efficiency
1900	4
1910	6
1920	8
1930	16
1940	18
1950	24
1960	30
1970	32
1980	34
1990	38

Analysis Questions

1. If a power plant is 32% efficient, what percentage of the energy input is lost?

2. Which decade(s) showed the greatest rate of change in efficiency?

3. What is the most likely estimate of power plant efficiency in 1955?

4. Based on improvements from 1900–1990, how efficient do you think a coal-burning power plant is today?

5. Answer the essential question: *What has been the efficiency trend over time for coal-burning power plants?*

Percent Efficiency

Essential Question: *What would you recommend to the operator of a coal-burning power plant to improve its efficiency?*

Overview

In the last activity, you saw that the percent efficiency of coal-burning power plants has increased over the last century. What is percent efficiency? Suppose a consulting firm for a power company presented you with the information in the diagram to the right. The diagram shows the energy exchanges for one day of operation at the plant.

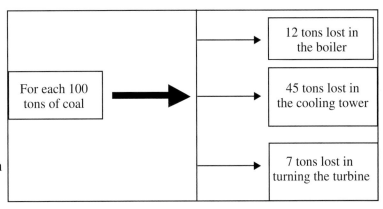

For each 100 tons of coal

12 tons lost in the boiler

45 tons lost in the cooling tower

7 tons lost in turning the turbine

In today's activity, you will use the information in this diagram and the input-output diagrams you have developed for other power plants. With this information, you will identify the ways energy is lost in the power plant.

Analysis Questions

1. Based on the diagram above, how much coal is actually converted into usable electricity?

2. What is the percent efficiency in the power plant represented in the diagram?

3. Refer to your group's input-output model of the different power plant systems from Lesson 3: *Power Plant Inputs and Outputs*. What kind of energy transformation is going on in the boiler? In the cooling tower? In the turbine?

4. There is energy lost in all three of these systems in the power plant. How do you think that energy is lost at each stage?

5. Answer the essential question: *What would you recommend to the operator of a coal-burning power plant to improve its efficiency?* Think of **three** ways to improve the efficiency of a coal-burning power plant. Your answer should relate to what you have learned about efficiency, but be creative and use evidence to support your ideas.

Efficient Technology

? *Essential Question:* What are the primary ways to improve efficiency in coal-burning power plants?

Overview

In this lesson, you will read about new technologies that are improving energy efficiency in coal-burning power plants.

Efficiency in Power Plants

Efficiency is a measure of how well energy is converted from one form to another and used. It is basically a ratio of the energy put into a system and the energy used by that system. Suppose light bulb "A" uses twice as much electricity as light bulb "B," but both light bulbs produce the same amount of light. Light bulb "B" is then twice as efficient as light bulb "A."

In power plants, efficiency is measured by the amount of energy produced compared to the energy contained in the burned fuel (for example, coal). By measuring production, you know the amount of coal you burn in the power plant. You also know the amount of energy that results from burning this amount of coal. (Energy is measured in British Thermal Units, or BTUs.) Therefore, you can calculate the amount of energy (in BTUs) you get from a given amount of coal. The more energy you can get and use from the fuel, the more efficient the power plant.

Older coal-burning power plants have an efficiency of about 30%. That means that 70% of the energy in burning coal is lost. Newer power plants are closer to 40% efficient. New technologies are being used to increase power plant efficiency in a variety of ways. Here are a few examples.

Cogeneration

Cogeneration is the production of both electricity and useful heat from the same fuel. It is also called "combined heat and power," or CHP. In a cogeneration plant, coal is burned in the usual way to produce electricity. However, the otherwise lost or "wasted" heat is put to other uses. Sometimes, the "waste" heat is used to boil water to create steam. The steam turns the turbine to create more electricity. The "waste" heat is also often used to heat power plant buildings. By using heat energy that would otherwise be lost in the combustion process, power plants increase efficiency.

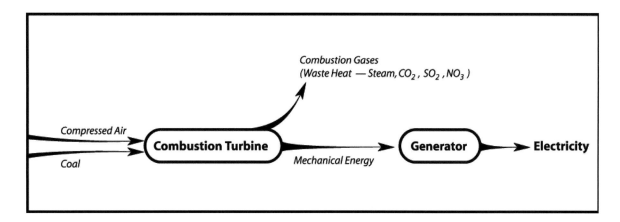

Sometimes, new systems are built into the older power plants. The result can be increased capacity (the amount of electricity generated) and efficiency. For example, an older coal-burning power plant may have a gas turbine built into its boiler system. As the coal is burning it is releasing gas. If the combustion of coal is performed in a gas turbine, then one of the byproducts of burning coal does not become waste. The gas that is formed can also produce electricity, thus increasing the efficiency. This add-on system can increase plant capacity by 30% and efficiency by 15%.

Combined Cycle Technology
In a combined cycle plant, the fuel is burned under high pressure. This reduces the amount of fuel needed for combustion. The hot, pressurized gas is then passed through a gas turbine. The turbine is connected to a generator to produce electricity. The hot gas from the turbine exhaust can be used to produce steam. Steam can also be produced directly from heat in the combustion chamber. That steam can run a turbine to produce more electricity. A "combined cycle" power plant is about 25% more efficient than a traditional plant.

Computer technology is also being used to increase power plant efficiency. Computers can monitor and control the combustion process more precisely. For example, computers can adjust combustion temperatures to the most efficient level.

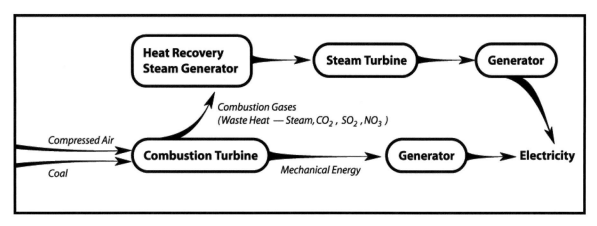

Fossil Fuels Forever?

It takes high temperatures, high pressures, and millions of years to turn organic matter into fossil fuel. This process limits the amount and availability of such resources. Fossil fuels are therefore considered a limited, or non-renewable resource. As the human population grows, the demand for electricity increases. This means the need for fossil fuels will grow as its supply dwindles.

The Energy Information Agency (EIA) is part of the U.S. Department of Energy. It analyzes energy reserves and predicts future demand for oil, coal and natural gas reserves until 2025. Below are some of its findings.

Oil. Oil will continue to be the dominant energy source worldwide. The world currently has between 1.5 and 2.0 trillion barrels of oil reserves. Demand for oil is expected to increase 1.9% per year from now until 2025. Oil production is currently 77 million barrels a day. By 2025, it will have to increase to 121 million barrels a day. Demand in the U.S., China, and the rest of Asia will account for at least 60% of this increase. Oil production, however, is expected to peak in 2010 and then decline steadily as reserves start to run out.

The world currently uses 28.1 billion barrels of oil per year. At a 1.9% per year increase in use, the world will be consuming 31.7 billion barrels of oil per year by 2010. By 2025, that usage will jump to 42.6 billion barrels of oil per year. At current usage, we have enough oil to last 71 1/2 years. At the predicted 2025 rate of usage, we have enough oil to last 45 years.

Coal. The world currently has about 984.6 billion tons of coal that can be recovered. Demand for coal is expected to increase 1.5% per year through 2025. Coal's share of total world energy is currently steady at about 24%. Coal use, which is mainly for electricity generation, is expected to decrease in Europe. However, it will greatly increase in Asia, especially in China and India. These two countries alone will account for 67% of the increased coal use.

In 2001, burning coal generated 64% of the world's electricity. Worldwide demand for electricity will grow at least 2.3% per year and nearly double by 2025. Some of this increased demand will be met by natural gas or renewable sources like wind. However, in Asia and other developing regions coal will be used to meet the demand.

Natural Gas. The world currently has about 155.7 trillion cubic meters of natural gas that can be recovered. Natural gas is the fastest-growing source of primary energy. Between 2000 and 2003, natural gas consumption increased about 67% to 151 trillion cubic feet per year. By 2025, the demand for natural gas is predicted to be 176 trillion cubic feet per year. It is also expected to surpass coal as the primary fuel for electricity generation by then.

Analysis Questions

1. Where in the process of electricity production is most energy lost?

2. What is cogeneration?

3. How does cogeneration improve the energy efficiency of power plants?

4. Answer the essential question: *What are the primary ways to improve efficiency in coal-burning power plants?*

Lesson 6

Consumer Energy Use

 Driving Question: How much electricity should we expect a family to use?

Overview

You now understand more about how a coal-burning power plant works. You saw in the last lesson that a power plant must meet changing consumer demand, which can vary with the seasons.

In this lesson, you will study consumer demand for energy. You will first explore your own personal energy use. You will compare your energy use to those of people who live in different eras. You will also compare it to the people who live in Wisconsin. In the process, you will learn ways you can personally conserve electricity. Understanding the amount of electricity people use will aid your decision concerning the power plant in Wisconsin. Perhaps with some changes in consumer use of energy, you could build a smaller power plant. In the next chapter, you will learn more about the environmental impacts of producing power using fossil fuels.

Important Content

•   Developed countries use more energy resources because of their lifestyles. They can decrease their demand with more efficient technology and conservation.

•   Your personal energy use is based on the choices you make every day.

Energy Inventory

Essential Questions: *Which appliances in your home use the most energy on an average day? What do those appliances have in common?*

Overview

When you woke up this morning, the first thing you heard was probably your electric alarm clock. When you took your morning shower, you may have used water that was heated in an electric hot water heater. Did you shave with an electric razor or blow-dry your hair? Did you check your e-mail before you left for school? On your way out the door, did you grab your cell phone from its charger? Did you take a waffle from the freezer and pop it in the toaster? If your family is like most American families, you use a lot of electricity every day. Do you know how much electricity you use? Do you know which appliances use the most electricity? Now that you know more about electricity, it's time to think about exactly how much electric energy you use in your home daily.

Materials

Household electricity bill (optional)

Household Appliance Spreadsheet
File Name: F5 Appliance Spreadsheet.xls
File Type: Microsoft Excel spreadsheet

Procedure

1. The Household Energy Use spreadsheet is a Microsoft Excel file. This sheet has been designed so that you only need to enter values in the green cells. Begin by entering your name and class at the top of the screen.

2. On the Household Energy Use Worksheet, you see a list of common household appliances. It includes their typical energy consumption rate, or wattage used. Fill in Column 1 on the worksheet. Record the number of each type of appliance you have in your home.

3. (Include any appliances in your home that are not on the worksheet. Write these in along with their typical energy consumption rate on the lines provided at the bottom of the worksheet. You can usually find the typical energy consumption rate (wattage) of an appliance on a tag or sticker on the back of the appliance. If the energy consumption rate listed is in watts, you will have to divide the number listed by 1000 to record the energy consumption rate in kilowatts.

4. Fill in Column 2 of the Household Energy Use Worksheet. Estimate the *average* number of hours *each appliance* in your home is in use on a typical day. Include the amount of time other family members use these appliances in addition to your own use. For example,

suppose one of your TVs is in the living room and is usually turned on for about 4 hours each day. The other TV in the kitchen is usually on for 6 hours each day. You should record the *average* number of hours each television is used per day. In this case, your family uses each TV for an average of 5 hours per day [because (6 hours + 4 hours)/2 = 5 hours]. So you would write "5 hours" in Column 2.

5. You know the typical rate of energy consumption for each appliance, the average amount of time you use each appliance, and the number of each type of appliance that you have in your home. The Microsoft Excel spreadsheet will calculate the total electrical energy used in your home on a typical day.

Here's how it works. Remember that watts are units representing an energy consumption rate. They are an amount of energy used over a length of time.

$$\text{Watts} = \frac{\text{amount of } Energy}{\text{length of } Time}$$

You are now looking for the total amount of energy used in a typical day. You want the units in your final answer to show amount of energy. Using some basic algebra, you can calculate that for each appliance.

Watts x length of *Time* = amount of *Energy*

Take the example of the televisions given above. The amount of energy used by all the TVs in the house on a typical day is:

2 TVs x .180 *kilowatts* x 5 *hours* = 1.8 *kilowatt hours*

6. Make a printout of your Household Energy Inventory spreadsheet and save the computer file. You'll need it again.

Analysis Questions

1. What is the total amount of energy your house uses on an average day?

2. (Optional) If you have access to your electric bill, multiply your answer to Question 1 by the number of days in the month on the bill. Compare your answer with the total electricity your home actually used. What was the difference (in kWh) between your calculations and the actual value on your family's bill? What may have caused this difference?

3. Look at the pie chart on the next page. It shows the typical breakdown of a household's energy use. How is this similar or different from energy use in your own home?

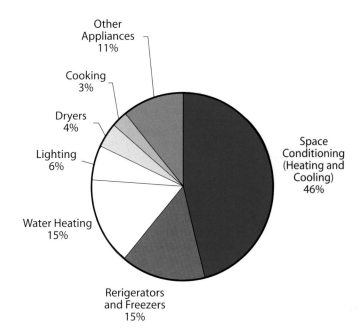

Other
Appliances
11%

Cooking
3%

Dryers
4%

Lighting
6%

Water Heating
15%

Rerigerators
and Freezers
15%

Space
Conditioning
(Heating and
Cooling)
46%

4. Answer the essential questions. *Which appliances in your home use the most energy on an average day? What do those appliances have in common?*

Historical Energy Use

Essential Question: *What might a family's energy inventory look like in the year 2015?*

Overview

In this age of technology, it seems like new inventions are announced every day. With each new electronic invention, the demand for electricity increases. This was not always the case. How do you think your lifestyle today differs from that of a typical family that lived in 1900 or 1950?

In this activity, you will read three short stories. Each describes how three families, living in different eras, used energy.

Procedure

Before reading each short story, make a table with three columns. Label the first column "Garcia, 2000," the second "Jones, 1950" and the third "Porter, 1900." Complete the table by listing all the appliances used in each story. After you have read all three stories, answer the analysis questions.

Story 1: The Garcia Family

The year is 2000. Jenny is a fifteen-year-old girl who lives in an apartment with her grandmother Rosa, her mother Maria, and her brother Tony.

Jenny has just arrived home from school. She walks into the kitchen, puts a snack into the toaster oven and immediately goes online with her computer to check her e-mail. She's expecting a note from her best friend Emery who just got a new DVD player. They've made plans to watch a movie at her house tomorrow after school. Tony is in the next room playing video games and listening to a new CD. His clock beeps at 5 o'clock, reminding him to start dinner before his mom gets home. He takes meat out of the freezer and defrosts it in the microwave. He then goes back to sit in front of the new 50-inch television to finish his video game. Rosa, Jenny's grandmother, is on the couch where she adjusts the reading light as she reads the newspaper. Jenny finishes checking her e-mail, and goes to the bathroom to try out a new hairstyle she read about online. After spending 15 minutes struggling with her curling iron and blow dryer, Jenny hears her mom enter the apartment. Jenny runs to vacuum her bedroom because she promised she would straighten up before her mom came home. Luckily, Jenny's mom goes straight to the laundry room to put a load of clothes into the washer. She doesn't hear Jenny vacuuming at the last minute. Once the wash is started, Maria heads for the kitchen and cooks the now defrosted meat on the electric stove. She then calls her children and her mother to the table for dinner.

Analysis Questions 1

1. What kinds of technologies do the Garcia's own and use on a regular basis?

2. How similar is their lifestyle to yours? How much energy do you think they use on average per day?

3. Estimate an energy inventory for the Garcia family. Refer to the inventory you did for your own energy use in Lesson 6: *Energy Inventory*.

Story 2: The Jones Family

The year is 1950. Helen Jones is a fifteen-year-old girl who lives in a one-story house. She lives with her parents, Mary and Tom, her older brother James, her younger sisters Elizabeth and Frances, and her baby brother Michael. Helen has just arrived home from school. She is excited about the new television her parents just purchased – the first in their neighborhood. Eager to see how it works, she turns on the television. She sees the face of Senator Benton of Connecticut delivering the first-ever political advertisement. Helen finds Senator Benton rather boring, so she walks over to the TV to see if anything better is on either of the other two channels.

While Helen is fidgeting with the antenna trying to tune in CBS, her mother and father are listening to news on the radio. Helen thinks her mom and dad are worried about the escalating cold war between the U.S. and the U.S.S.R. Elizabeth and Francis are playing with some toys in the living room and Michael is asleep in the bassinet.

1950 Zenith G2438R 16" B&W Screen (USA)

James is in his bedroom, listening to the newest Bing Crosby album on his record player. He's getting ready to go to that night's school dance. Tom is letting James borrow the car to pick up his friends at the nearby diner and then drive to the dance. As James gets ready to go, he throws on his jacket and combs his hair a few more times. As he admires himself in the mirror, he thinks to himself that he looks a lot like the movie star Spencer Tracy. James turns out the light in his room, says goodbye to his parents, and heads out the door.

A few minutes later, Mary heads into the kitchen. She looks through the refrigerator and takes out some meat to cook for dinner. Tom turns off the radio and heads down to the basement to tinker with his elaborate electric train set, his favorite hobby. Meanwhile, Helen is ironing the shirt she will wear the next day to school.

Analysis Questions 2

1. List the appliances that the Jones family used most.

2. How do you think these appliances and technologies differ from the ones we have today?

3. How do you think the Jones's lifestyle differs from yours or that of the Garcia family?

4. How many family members live in the Jones household? How do you think their amount of energy use would differ from that of the Garcia family of four?

5. Assume that the wattage of the appliances is equal to those we use now. Estimate the number of kWh (kilowatt-hours) the Jones family would use per day.

Story 3: The Porter Family

The year is 1900. Charles is a fifteen-year-old boy who lives in an apartment building with his parents and five brothers and sisters. He has just come home from the wood-working factory where he works the night shift. His income from the factory supplements his father's income and helps support his mother, brothers, and sisters. Charles brings a newspaper home for his father, who skims through it (it's the only form of news they have). Charles' father is intrigued by all the new inventions he reads about in the paper, especially something called a light bulb. The paper says the light bulb could soon replace the oil-burning lamps in the apartment. Charles' mother is getting ready to go to the post office to send a telegram to her sister who lives on the other coast. The post office is the only place in the neighborhood that has a telegraph. Before she leaves, Charles' mother looks in the icebox and notices that the ice has melted and the milk is nearly spoiled. She will have to walk to the store to buy more milk and ice on her way home. Meanwhile, Charles is watching over his brothers and sisters. He's daydreaming about the next night when his family plans to take an outing to a theater where they will see a live stage show!

Analysis Questions 3

1. How is the Porter's lifestyle different from the Jones family lifestyle? The Garcia's?

2. What kinds of energy did the Porter family rely on?

3. Think about the differences in the Porter family, the Jones family, and the Garcia family. What trends in technology use and energy use do you see across the different time periods?

4. Answer the essential question: *What might a family's energy inventory look like in the year 2015?* Create a rough energy inventory for a family of four in the year 2015. Will your life then be much different than it is today? How will technology and electricity usage differ from that of today?

How much is Reasonable?

Essential Question: *If consumers are more energy efficient, can they decrease the demand for electricity so that it meets the amount we can generate with fossil fuels?*

Overview

Brownouts and blackouts have taught us that the supply of electricity cannot always keep up with the demand. When that happens, the price of electricity may increase dramatically. Rolling blackouts may become a routine.

One way we can change this is by reducing the amount of energy used in our daily lives. Using more efficient appliances can reduce the amount of electricity we use. We can also be careful about how often we are using electricity. We can turn off lights when we leave rooms. We can use air conditioning only when it's absolutely necessary. In today's lesson, you will look at your personal electricity use and try to reduce it. Based on the sacrifices you are able to make, you will predict the energy use for a family of four in Wisconsin

Materials

your complete Household Energy Use Worksheet from Lesson 6: *Energy Inventory* (or the computer file you created)

Household Appliance Spreadsheet
File Name: F5 Appliance Spreadsheet.xls
File Type: Microsoft Excel spreadsheet

Analysis Questions

1. One simple thing people do to reduce their electricity use is to change their light bulbs from regular (incandescent) bulbs to fluorescent bulbs. On the Excel Appliance worksheet, see how much electricity you would save by replacing all your regular bulbs with fluorescent bulbs.

2. Look at the table on the next page. It shows the typical energy savings you can achieve by using more efficient appliances. On the Excel Appliance worksheet, see how much electricity you would save by replacing your current appliances with more efficient ones. (To do this, use the blank lines at the bottom of the worksheet. Enter the efficient appliances and their electricity use there.)

3. Another simple way to save energy is to reduce the number of hours that lights and appliances are left on. Think about the number of lights and appliances that are left on in your home when they are not in use. Change the numbers in your spreadsheet to reflect the number of hours that appliances are being used. See how much this saves you.

4. *What are reasonable electricity needs for a family of four in Wisconsin?* To answer this, adjust the numbers from your own family to match a family of four. Keep in mind: Wisconsin has hot summers and cold winters. Most families there live in single-family homes, not apartments.

5. Answer the essential question: *If consumers are more energy efficient, can they decrease the demand for electricity so that it meets the amount we can generate with fossil fuels?* Use your calculations from Lesson 5: *Efficient Technology* to answer this question.

Efficient Appliances

Appliance	Typical Consumption Rate	Efficient Consumption Rate
Refrigerator - Freezer	0.500	0.300
Refrigerator - Side by Side	0.900	0.540
Air Conditioner (central)	3.500	3.150
Air Conditioner (room - 6000 BTU)	0.750	0.685
Dishwasher	2.400	1.800
Clothes Washer	0.500	0.250

Impacts

Chapter 3
Impacts

Connections

The increasing demand for electricity in Wisconsin will require the community to build an additional power plant. To understand the costs of building this power plant, it is necessary to understand how burning fossil fuels can affect the environment. In the last chapter, you learned how fossil fuels are burned to generate electricity. In this chapter, you will look at the impacts on the environment of burning those fossil fuels. You will use this information in the next chapter to help you make a decision about the best location for a coal-burning power plant in the Lake Geneva, Wisconsin area.

In this chapter:

You will start with an overview of the types of emissions produced by fossil fuel power plants. You will do a few labs to identify the products of the combustion. You will see the effects these products have on the world around you. You will examine the air in your school to see if it contains particle pollutants, some of which may come from fossil fuel power plants. You will read about other effects of fossil fuel power plants, and study their effect on the lakes that the plants draw water from. You will refer back what you learned in Chapter 2 about how power plants work as you go through this chapter. Finally, you will determine how far the effects of power plant operations can spread.

When you're done you'll be able to:

• Describe the atmospheric emissions of fossil fuel power plants;

• Determine the area affected by a power plant's emissions;

• Predict the amount of water a power plant needs to operate;

• Analyze how a lake from which a power plant withdraws water will be affected by this use.

Lesson 1
Combustion of Fossil Fuels

Driving Question: What are all the products of burning fossil fuels?

Overview

In the last chapter, you looked at fossil fuel power plants and their inputs and outputs. However, one thing was omitted from that discussion. In addition to outputs like electricity and steam, fossil fuel power plants also have other, less desirable outputs. Burning coal releases polluting gases and particles into the air and also ash. Ash is the substance that is left after the coal has been burned. The polluting gases and particles are released into the air when coal is burned whereas, the ash that is left must be disposed of somehow. Coal-burning power plants have other environmental impacts as well, such as their affect on land. The site where a new power plant is built affects the natural ecosystem of that area. Also, transporting the coal from the mine to the power plant affects land use.

In this lesson, you will begin to explore the impacts of burning fossil fuels. In a lab experiment, you will look at the chemistry of combustion. Where you will learn about the unintended outputs of burning coal. You will then return to your computer model of a coal-burning power plant to discover how controlling these outputs affect the way decisions are made about meeting the demand for electricity.

Important Content

- The combustion of coal creates byproducts that can be harmful. These include carbon dioxide, carbon monoxide, nitrogen oxides, sulfur dioxide, mercury, and particulates.

- Advances in technology can be used to control pollution and reduce environmental impacts.

Impacts

Side Effects

Essential Question: *Which consequences must be studied to understand how far the effects from coal-burning power plants will spread?*

Overview

In the last chapter, you listed all of the inputs to fossil fuel power plants. You also listed all of the resources needed to build and maintain a power plant. The main output of the power plant is electricity for human use, but what are the other outputs?

In this activity, you will begin to explore the effects that coal-burning power plants have on the environment. You know how power plants work and how energy is transformed. Now you will describe the direct effects these inputs and outputs have on the environment. In the activities that follow, you will explore how each step in the process of generating electricity impacts the physical environment and other living things.

Procedure

1. Split up into groups assigned by your teacher. With your group, fill out the worksheet "Impacts of Burning Coal." For each activity involved in the building and operation of a coal-burning power plant, write down the impacts you predict it might have on the environment. Predict how far you think those effects will spread (i.e., Will it affect only the area right around the power plant? Cities near the power plant? The whole state? The world?). If you aren't sure how far the impact will spread, write "not sure" in the box.

2. After you have completed the worksheet, answer the analysis questions.

3. Read the essay at the end of this lesson.

Analysis Questions

1. Which of the effects you listed in the worksheet will be limited to the location of the power plant? Which ones will definitely occur in a different location? Which ones might have a widespread impact?

2. The power plant built in Wisconsin might have negative environmental effects in a distant state. Who should pay for the cost of repairing or preventing those effects? Why?

3. Answer the essential question: *Which consequences must be studied to understand how far the effects from coal-burning power plants will spread?*

Impacts of Burning Coal

Activity	Effects	How far will this effect spread?
Building the Power Plant		
Mining Coal		
Transporting Coal (train, road)		
Burning Coal (generating power)		
Disposing of Ash/Waste		
Using Water		
Any other activities or effects?		

What are the impacts of building and using coal power plants?

Let's review all the steps involved in generating electricity by burning coal. The first thing you need to generate electricity is a power plant. You have to build the plant, move materials from other locations, clear land and build. The next thing you need is coal. Coal is mined underground or in strip mines. It must then be transported to the power plant. Coal power plants also require water for steam to turn the generator and for cooling. This water is collected from a nearby lake or river. The burning of coal produces gases and particles that must either be released into the atmosphere or trapped and disposed of in some other way.

The process of building a power plant changes the physical environment. Roads must be built, and buildings constructed. The same effects are seen where coal is mined. The land is cleared of trees and other vegetation to get the coal from the ground. Coal mining also releases methane (CH_4) into the atmosphere.

A 350 MW power plant requires 900 liters of water per second for cooling. Some of this water is returned to the lake or river it originally came from, but much of it enters the atmosphere through evaporation. The water power plants do return to lakes may be slightly warmer than when it was taken from the lake or river. This change in water temperature can affect the aquatic ecosystem in the lake or river.

Burning pure coal produces carbon dioxide (CO_2) and water (H_2O) gases, which are released into the atmosphere. The coal that is burned in power plants contains impurities, such as sulfur, nitrogen, and mercury. These impurities are either released into the atmosphere as the coal burns or trapped by various kinds of filters on the power plant. The coal that does not burn completely ends up as ash and small particles.

Each of these direct effects of burning coal to generate electricity can have an impact on the physical environment and on other living things. Some of these impacts are focused in a small area and others are spread over large areas. All of them can be minimized or prevented through the use of technologies.

Combustion

Essential Question: Other than heat, what are the outputs of combustion?

Overview

A major source of air pollution is combustion–the process of burning. In this activity, you will investigate what happens to a variety of materials as they burn.

Materials

safety goggles
2 wads of cotton
1 jar lid or crucible
1 600 mL beaker
4 matches
1 medicine dropper
1 wad of wool
1 piece Styrofoam®
2 drops turpentine

Safety

Wear your goggles and lab apron. Follow standard safety rules for using glassware or working with matches. Tie back long hair, and tie back or remove any article of clothing or jewelry that can hang down and touch chemicals or flames. Never taste anything involved in an experiment and never directly smell the source of any vapor or gas.

Procedure

1. Make a data table that lists the following: the material you burned, the color of the smoke when burned, the odor of the smoke, the observed products, and any other observations you can make.

2. Place a small wad of cotton in a crucible.

3. Use a match or lighter to set the cotton on fire. Cover the lid and burning cotton with the 600 mL beaker. If the flame begins to go out before the cotton is fully burned, lift the edge of the beaker slightly to let in more air.

4. When the flame goes out, observe the beaker and the products of combustion. Record your observations on the data table. Take the beaker to the window to allow the fumes to escape.

5. Obtain a fresh cotton wad, and rinse out and dry your beaker. Use the medicine dropper to place two drops of turpentine on the cotton. Turpentine is an accelerant and increases the rate of combustion. Compare the amount and color of the products you collect with and without the use of an accelerant. Repeat the above steps for burning and observation. Record your results.

6. Repeat the above steps for burning wool and Styrofoam. Do not inhale the fumes. They are poisonous.

7. Clean up your materials.

Analysis Questions

1. Which of the materials burned the fastest? Which produced the brightest flame?

2. Which of these materials do you think would give off the most energy if burned in a power plant? Why?

3. Which materials gave off the most air pollution? What evidence do you have to support your conclusion?

4. Describe how you could change this experiment to produce better evidence to support your answer to Question 3.

5. Answer the essential question: *Other than heat, what are the outputs of combustion?*

Chemistry of Coal Combustion

Essential Question: Why should we concerned about the byproducts of burning fossil fuel?

Overview

Read the following article and answer the analysis questions below.

The Chemistry of Combustion

The burning of fossil fuels to generate electricity has a very large impact on the environment. Power plants are responsible for 40% of all human–caused emissions of carbon dioxide (CO_2), 64% of all emissions of sulfur dioxide (SO_2), and 26% of all emission of nitrogen oxides (NO_x). They also emit carbon monoxide (CO). These substances (CO_2, CO, SO_2, and NO_x) are byproducts of the burning of coal.

Burning is also called combustion. For combustion to occur, oxygen must be present. When combustion occurs, energy, in the form of heat, is released, and other byproducts such as light, CO_2, and water vapor are produced. Power plants that burn fossil fuels are not the only source of byproduct emissions. All sources of combustion, such as car engines and gas stoves emit CO_2 and other byproducts.

Carbon Dioxide

Coal consists primarily of carbon (C). When coal is burned in a power plant, oxygen in the air combines with the carbon to produce carbon dioxide and heat. The chemical equation for the combustion of carbon is: $C + O_2 \rightarrow CO_2 + $ energy (heat). The heat produced in a power plant is used to convert water to steam. The rapid expansion of the steam is used to turn turbines that are connected to electricity generators. The carbon dioxide that is produced is released into the atmosphere, where it can travel over large distances. Carbon dioxide is not usually considered a pollutant because it is not harmful to living things. In fact, carbon dioxide is essential to plants, which use it to produce their food through photosynthesis. However, scientists have grown concerned about increasing levels of carbon dioxide in the atmosphere and the long-term effect of increased carbon dioxide emissions on the climate. You will study carbon dioxide emissions and their effect on the environment in **Chapter 5: Global Climate Change**.

Carbon Monoxide

If coal is not burned efficiently because there is not enough oxygen available or because the air temperature is below a certain level, then carbon monoxide is produced. Carbon monoxide is an odorless gas that is harmful to humans and other animals. When inhaled, carbon monoxide gets in the bloodstream and interferes with the body's use of oxygen. In high concentrations, such as those that result when running a car in a closed garage, carbon monoxide can be fatal. In the lower concentrations that result from power plant or automobile emissions into the atmosphere, carbon monoxide can cause fatigue and aggravate existing health problems like heart disease. The elderly, young people, and people with weakened respiratory systems are particularly sensitive to carbon monoxide. Carbon monoxide can also react with other pollutants to create ground-level ozone, which is also harmful to the respiratory system of humans and other animals.

Sulfur Dioxide

All coal contains some impurities. When coal burns, its impurities are also oxidized. Sulfur is one of the most common impurities in coal. Sulfur is a yellowish substance that occurs in all coal in generally small amounts. Coal mined from the eastern U.S. contains from 3 to 10% sulfur (by weight of coal). Coal mined in western states usually has less than 1% sulfur (by weight of coal). These variations in sulfur content result from differences in the type of vegetation that decomposed to form the coal, the age of the coal, and the geology of the surrounding area. The sulfur in coal occurs in two forms — organic and pyretic. Organic sulfur is connected to the carbon in coal. Pyretic sulfur is found in inorganic compounds that are trapped in the coal, but are not bound to the carbon. Both forms of sulfur can react with oxygen to form sulfur dioxide by the reaction:

$$S + O_2 \rightarrow SO_2$$

In the atmosphere, SO_2 is a colorless gas that irritates the lungs. The major environmental impact resulting from sulfur dioxide emissions is acid deposition. Acid deposition occurs when sulfur dioxide reacts with other chemicals in the atmosphere to create acidic precipitation (wet deposition) or acidic gases (dry deposition). As you will learn in Lesson 3 of this chapter, acid deposition can be harmful to ecosystems and can hasten weathering and erosion of rocks.

Nitrogen Oxides

Nitrogen (N_2) and oxygen (O_2) are the most abundant components of the air we breathe. Nitrogen and oxygen make up nearly 99% of the atmosphere. They both occur naturally in the atmosphere as two atoms bonded together. When air is heated to extremely high temperatures, as in a coal burner, the oxygen atoms break apart. The individual oxygen atoms can chemically re-bond to form O_2 again. They can also combine with nitrogen molecules to form NO, or nitric oxide. Some nitric oxide is quickly converted in the atmosphere to NO_2 (nitrogen dioxide), which is the gas that gives smog its brownish color. NO and NO_2 are often referred to as "NO_x" (rhymes with "fox"). NO_x can also be formed from the nitrogen molecules that are trapped inside coal. The chemical reactions for NO formation are:

Production of Nitric Oxide:

$$O_2 + heat \rightarrow 2O$$

$$O + N_2 \rightarrow \mathbf{NO} + N$$

Production of Nitrogen Dioxide:

$$N + O_2 \rightarrow NO + O$$

$$O + NO \rightarrow \mathbf{NO_2}$$

NO and NO_2 are air pollutants and are harmful to breathe. In addition, they can react with other chemicals in the atmosphere, to create ground-level ozone. Like sulfur dioxide, nitrogen oxides also contribute to acid deposition.

(NO_x) can be produced by any fuel that burns at a high enough temperature. Automobiles, for example, produce NO_x when they burn gasoline. .

Reducing emissions from combustion

It is not possible to eliminate byproducts from combustion because they are the inevitable result of oxidation. However, it is possible to reduce or eliminate the environmental impacts of these emissions.

Carbon dioxide

Until recently, carbon dioxide was considered a harmless byproduct of combustion. There is no way to prevent the production of carbon dioxide in combustion. However, scientists are beginning to explore the possibility of capturing the carbon dioxide that is created in the combustion of fossil fuels like coal before it is emitted into the atmosphere. They are exploring the possibility of storing carbon dioxide underground, where it would not affect climate. This technique is not currently feasible but may be feasible in the future.

Carbon monoxide

The production of carbon monoxide from fossil fuel combustion can be minimized by maintaining a high temperature in the combustion chamber and insuring a sufficient flow of oxygen into the chamber.

Sulfur dioxide

There are three methods used to prevent sulfur dioxide emissions from entering the atmosphere. The first method is simply to use coal containing less sulfur, like the coal found in western states. If there is less sulfur in the coal, less SO_2 gas is produced during combustion.

The second method is called *washing*. Washing is used to remove pyretic sulfur (the sulfur present in compounds) from coal. This process removes the sulfur from the coal before the coal is burned. One way this is done is by crushing the coal into small chunks and washing it. During the process, coal chunks are fed into a large water-filled tank. The coal floats to the surface while the sulfur impurities sink to the bottom. Facilities that wash coal this way are called "coal preparation plants."

Not all sulfur can be removed by washing. Organic sulfur is usually removed by the third method, called flue gas desulfurization. This process takes place in "scrubbers," which "scrub" the sulfur out of the smoke released by the power plant. This method takes place after the coal is burned, when the sulfur has oxidized to make sulfur dioxide. In most scrubbers, limestone is mixed with water. The mixture is sprayed into the coal combustion gases called "flue gases." The limestone captures the sulfur and absorbs it. The limestone and sulfur combine to form either a wet paste, or in some newer scrubbers, a dry powder. The sulfur is trapped and does not escape into the atmosphere. The paste or powder is usually disposed of in a landfill. This is the most common method used for removing sulfur from coal.

Nitrogen Oxides

Coal-burning power plants have always produced large amounts of NO_x. However, scientists and engineers have developed new ways to reduce this pollutant at the source. One of the best ways to reduce NO_x is to prevent it from forming in the first place. This can be done two ways. The first is by reducing the amount of extra air (including nitrogen) that is in the power plant's boiler. The other is by keeping the temperature of the burners as low as possible. If there is less nitrogen available, most of the oxygen in the air combines with the fuel, not with the nitrogen. If the temperature in the burner is lower, less NO_x will form. One problem with this method is it also decreases the efficiency of the power plant. There is also new "scrubber" technology that cleans NO_x from the flue gases. Some of these devices also add chemicals to convert the NO_x into fertilizers. These scrubbers are more expensive than low-NO_x burners, but they remove up to 90% of NO_x pollutants from power plant emissions

Tradeoffs

While technologies can substantially reduce the quantity of harmful emissions from the combustion of coal and other fossil fuels, they also increase the cost of power generation and reduce the efficiency of power plants. You will explore these tradeoffs in upcoming activities. It is also important to remember that another way to reduce harmful emissions is to reduce the quantity of fossil fuels burned by reducing the demand for energy.

Analysis Questions

1. What is combustion? How is it related to the production of power plant air pollutants?

2. List the main byproducts of burning coal that contribute to air pollution. Describe why each is present in a coal-burning power plant. Explain how each is produced and each one's environmental effects.

3. Explain how "scrubbers" and other technologies can reduce air pollutants emitted by coal-burning power plants.

4. Answer the essential question: *Why should we concerned about the byproducts of burning fossil fuels?*

Modeling Combustion

Essential Question: *Why is it difficult for power companies to reduce emissions and still be profitable?*

Overview

Combustion releases pollutants into the air. You have read about the three main pollutants – CO_2, SO_2, and NO_x – that are released when coal is burned. You have also read about the ways that two of these emissions – SO_2 and NO_x – can be reduced with "scrubbers" and other technologies. If you were the director of a power plant, would you install this technology to reduce air pollution? In this activity, you will return to your role as director of a power plant. You need to meet the demands of your customers, but you also must keep emissions low. You also need to make money. You will have to decide which of these factors are most important as you as you operate the plant. If you decide to release emissions into the air, there will be consequences, like acidic deposition and smog.

Materials

Coal Power Plant Model
File Name: Coal Power Plant Model
File Type: application program

Procedure 1: Amount of Coal

1. As in your last model, you can adjust the amount of coal you burn to generate electricity. Open the Coal Power Plant Model but this time, select multiple emissions at startup.

2. Click the **Start** button. Adjust the coal-burning rate and watch the effect in the generator. Describe it in your notebook.

> **Stop and Think**
>
> When you increase coal-burning rate, what happens to amount of electricity generated? Why?

Procedure 2: Finances of Coal Burning

1. Explore the business part of the model. Your power plant needs to make money to pay your employees and make a profit. Reset the model and start it again. Watch what happens to the cost when you burn more or less coal. Describe this.

2. In your own words, describe the relationship between the amount of coal burned and the income of the power plant.

> **Stop and Think**
>
> What would happen to the power plant's bank account if you changed the price of electricity? How would consumers react to a price change? In this activity, you cannot change the price of electricity.

Procedure 3: Including Emission

1. Now see what happens when you include SO_2 emissions and SO_2 controls. From your reading, what are three ways to reduce SO_2 emissions?

2. When you move the SO_2 control slider up, you are using one of those three methods to reduce SO_2 emissions. Describe what happens to your bank account when you use more SO_2 controls?

3. Play with the sliders to adjust the coal-burning rate and the SO_2 controls. What do you observe? Describe your observations.

4. Activate NO_x controls on the model. As you increase the NO_x controls, you are increasing the number of scrubbers at work in the plant.

5. Explore the whole model by adjusting the coal-burning rate and the NO_x and SO_2 controls. Describe what you see.

Analysis Questions

1. Describe the relationship between NO_x controls and NO_x emissions.

2. Describe the relationship between NO_x controls and bank account balance.

3. Answer the essential question: *Why is it difficult for power companies to reduce emissions and still be profitable?*

Coal Plant Operations

 Essential Question: *Why might a power company choose to violate emissions standards?*

Overview

This activity presents the real test of your operational skills. As director of operations, you will have to run the power plant under three different situations: winter, summer, and peak summer. You will have to meet electricity demand, make money, and not violate emission standards for SO_2 and NO_2.

Materials

 Coal Power Plant Model
File Name: Coal Power Plant Model
File Type: Application Program

Procedure

There are several rules you must follow.

- You are expected to keep sulfur dioxide (SO_2) emissions at or below 20 kg/hour. You are also expected to keep nitrogen oxide (NO_x) emissions at or below 20 kg/hour. If you don't, you must pay a severe penalty to the state's Energy Facility Council.

- You need to produce 10% more electricity than the demand at any time. This will prevent customers from experiencing brownouts or blackouts.

- You must keep careful records of your actions in case of audits. Record required data in a table.

Situations

A. The average demand for electricity during winter months is 115 MWh. Try to generate at least 10% more electricity at your power plant than the demand without violating emission standards.

B. The average demand for electricity during the summer months is 125 MWh. Try to generate at least 10% more electricity at your power plant than the demand without violating emission standards.

C. During summer months, the region often experiences a heat wave where temperatures are well above normal. During this time, the demand for electricity increases to 150 MWh to supply energy for air conditioning. Try to generate at least 10% more electricity at your power plant than the demand without violating emission standards.

Analysis Questions

1. In what situations was it difficult to make a profit and meet emissions regulations?

2. What are some ways you could continue to make money during heat waves? Would you choose to do these things or not? Why?

3. The emissions regulations for power plants only specify the amount of emissions allowed per year. If the plant has more emissions at one point during the year, they may balance that with fewer emissions at another time. What strategies could you use to balance summer and winter emissions while still meeting demand?

4. Scrubber technology reduces the amount of SO_2 and NO_x pollution. In most power plants, the technology cannot be changed on a day-to-day basis. The power plant first must decide what level of protection is needed. They must then install the equipment and use only that system for the life of the power plant. How would you decide what level of protection to put on your power plant? (Remember, the more advanced and efficient the scrubber, the more it costs.)

5. Answer the essential question: *Why might a power company choose to violate emissions standards?*

Coal Plant Operations • Data Table

Make sure you include units with all numbers!

Situation	Electricity Needed (10% above demand)	Coal Burning Rate	Electricity Generated	SO2 emissions	NOx emissions	Bank Balance
(letter)	(MW)	(rate)	(MW)	(kg/hr)	(kg/hr	(increasing or decreasing)
Winter (A)						
Summer (B)						
Heat wave (C)						

Other Sources of Emissions

Essential Question: What human activities contribute to air pollution emissions?

Overview

In the last few activities, you learned about the byproducts of coal combustion, including sulfur dioxide (SO_2) and nitrogen oxides (NO_x). Fossil fuel power plants, particularly coal plants, are major producers of these two polluting chemicals. However, they are not the only sources of these emissions Look at the pie charts on the next page to see other sources of SO_2 and NO_x emissions in the U.S.

Analysis Questions

1. What activity is responsible for most of the SO_2 emissions?

2. What activity is most responsible for NO_x emissions?

3. What percent of the SO_2 emissions are due to some type of burning or combustion? From which activity do these emissions come?

4. What percent of the NO_x emissions are due to combustion? From which activity do they come?

5. Suppose you wanted to reduce the amount of SO_2 in the atmosphere. Based on the graphs on the next page, would it be better to change the way power plants are run or the number of miles people drive in their cars? If you wanted to reduce NO_x emissions, would you take the same actions?

6. Answer the essential question: *What human activities contribute to air pollution emissions?*

U.S. SO$_x$ Emissions in 1992
(22.7 Million Tons)

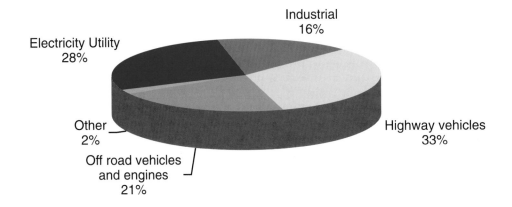

Industrial
16%

Electricity Utility
28%

Other
2%

Highway vehicles
33%

Off road vehicles
and engines
21%

U.S. NO$_x$ Emissions in 1992
(23.3 Million Tons)

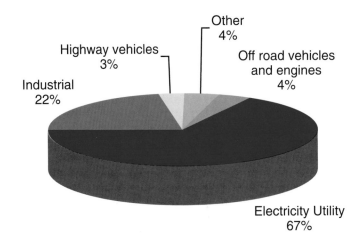

Other
4%

Highway vehicles
3%

Off road vehicles
and engines
4%

Industrial
22%

Electricity Utility
67%

Lesson 2
Ash and Particulates

Driving Question: *Should we be concerned about the particles of dust released from power plants?*

Overview

In the previous lesson, you learned that coal-burning power plants release the gases SO_2, NO_x, CO_2, CO, and mercury into the atmosphere. All of these are pollutants, meaning they are harmful to living things. Coal power plants also release ash and tiny particles, called particulates, into the air. Dust particles are in the air all the time. Sometimes, you can see them when floating in the air when the Sun shines brightly through them. Many dust particles are harmless, but some of the particles that come from power plants can be very harmful. Coal-burning power plants are not the only source of these harmful particles, but they do contribute greatly to the problem. In this lesson, you will use a collector to see measure the particulates in the air in in different locations in your school. You will also read about the harmful effects of particulates. In particular, you will learn about mercury, which can be present in the particulates released by burning coal. Mercury in the environment presents a serious health hazard to humans and other animals.

Lesson Goals

- The area affected by a power plant is larger than the power plant itself. In fact, a power plant can have impacts over hundreds of miles.

- Particulates from power plants can include toxic substances like mercury, which can poison aquatic life.

Collecting Particulates

Essential Questions: Where in your school would you expect to find the most particulates? Where would you expect to find the fewest particulates?

Overview

Particulates are extremely small solid particles and liquid droplets suspended in the air. Particulates that naturally occur in the air we breathe include dust, soil, volcanic ash, pollen, and sea salt. The increase of particulates in the atmosphere caused by human activity is now a concern because of the health problems they can cause. Particulates that result from human activities include soil particles from plowing and overgrazing of arid land, mineral dust from mining, ash from oil and coal-burning power plants, ash and smoke from factories, emissions from vehicles (particularly those that burn diesel fuel), and ash from fireplaces and stoves that burn wood or coal.

In this activity, you will create collectors to capture particulates in the air around your school.

Materials

2 index cards per student
tape to cover cards
tape or tacks to attach cards to observation points
digital balance (scale)

Safety

Follow standard safety rules and school safety rules for laboratory activities.

Procedure

1. Attach tape to each index card so the tape is facing sticky side out.

2. Use the digital balance to determine the mass of each index card covered with tape. Record this mass on your data table.

3. As a group, decide where to place your index cards. You should place half of them in places you think are likely to collect lots of particulates. You should place the other half in places you think are free from particulates. Record your locations.

4. Check your cards every two days for a week. Record your observations in your data table.

5. You will continue this experiment later in this lesson, in the activity called *Analyzing Particulates.*

Analysis Questions

1. How did your group decide where to place your index cards?

2. Answer the essential questions: *Where in your school would you expect to find the most particulates? Where would you expect to find the fewest particulates?*

Particulate Danger

Essential Question: What do particulates have to do with me?

Overview

In this lesson, you will read about the health effects of tiny particles produced by coal-burning power plants and other sources.

Particulate Danger

We are all familiar with ash. You know that when you burn wood, some ashes remain. Some type of ash is always produced when carbon-based fuels, like wood and coal, are burned. The smallest bits of ash, the ones that can stay suspended in the air for extended periods of time, are called *particulates*. Ash particulates are tiny, even microscopic. In recent years, studies have linked certain particulates to serious human health problems. They have found that these problems are most common in cities downwind from coal-burning power plants and where diesel engines are in use.

Particulates from burning plant matter and fossil fuels are rarely particles of pure carbon. They often have other harmful or toxic substances attached to them. Chemicals found on particulates include sulfates, heavy metals, and volatile organic compounds. Sulfates are acidic forms of sulfur that can damage lungs. Heavy metals are naturally occurring elements, such as lead, cadmium, and nickel, that can be harmful to people and other animals. Volatile organic compounds (VOCs), such as benzene and ethylene, result from incomplete burning of fossil fuels.

Particulates are classified by size. Particulate size is measured in microns. A micron is a length equal to one-millionth of a meter or 1/1000 of a millimeter. Particles greater than 10 microns in diameter cannot enter the lungs, so they pose the least health hazard. These "large" particulates usually settle in the mouth or nose. Particles less than 10 microns in size can be inhaled. These may enter the lungs, but usually do not enter far beyond the upper airway. Still, the irritation that they cause can lead to asthma attacks and other respiratory problems. The tiniest "fine" particulates pose the most serious danger to health. These microscopic particulates are able to penetrate deeply into the lungs and enter the bloodstream. They take more time for the body to expel and can cause very serious damage.

Johns Hopkins School of Public Health in Baltimore, Maryland, analyzed death rates in 20 large cities between 1987 and 1994. The researchers found that the death rate in an area due to lung disease was directly related to the number of fine particulates in the air there. Even small amounts were found to affect health. The higher the concentration of fine particulates in the air, the higher the human death rate.

Particulate concentrations are measured by how many particulates occur in a cubic meter of air. The Environmental Protection Agency (EPA) allows a maximum level of 150 micrograms of fine particulates per cubic meter of air within a 24-hour period. All cities covered in the Johns Hopkins study averaged levels only one-third that much. Some averaged even less than that. Yet all showed health problems caused by fine particulates in the air.

The Johns Hopkins study found that for each increase of 10 micrograms per cubic meter of air, the death rate rose about one-half of 1% (0.5%). Studies conducted in British Colombia, Canada, showed a 1% rise in the death rate for every 10 microgram increase per cubic meter. So, if a city's concentration of fine particulates increases by 20 micrograms per cubic meter, two additional deaths occur for each 100 deaths in the city. These studies focused only on deaths from lung disease. Researchers are also considering the death rate if heart disease deaths are included in these figures. Early estimates indicate the death rate would rise 3.4% with heart disease deaths included.

Other researchers have estimated that 64,000 Americans a year die early from inhalation of fine particulates. A 1998 British study concluded that inhalation of fine particulates was more dangerous than smoking. The study concluded it raised the death rate from lung cancer by 8%.

Even short-term exposure to fine particulates can be deadly. The World Health Organization (WHO) found that short-term exposure increased respiratory illness in children by 7 to 10%. Short-term exposure was estimated to increase the total death rate by 1.6%. That estimate rose to 3.4% in cities with the most polluted air.

What do coal-burning power plants have to do with fine particulates? Coal-burning power plants account for more than 23% of all particulates emitted into the air. In 1997, coal-burning power plants released more than 290 tons of particulates into the atmosphere. This was more than any other fuel combustion source. However, coal plants are not the largest source of particulate emissions. Industrial processes, including chemical and oil refining, emit more particulates than all forms of fossil fuel combustion combined. A large proportion also comes from soil erosion and dust.

New technologies have been developed in recent years that can trap as much as 99.8% or more of the particulates present in coal emissions. These technologies are increasingly being used. However, just like other pollution control technologies, they add to the cost of electricity generation.

Analysis Questions

1. What are the sources of particulates in the air?

2. Why are fine particulates far more dangerous to human health than large particulates?

3. How do coal-burning power plants contribute to particulate pollution?

4. Suppose the concentration of fine particulates increased in southeastern Wisconsin. What types of health problems would you predict would become more common among the city's residents?

5. Answer the essential question: *What do particulates have to do with me?*

Analyzing Particulates

Essential Question: How are particulates distributed around your school?

Overview

In this activity, you will analyze the data you collected with the particulate collectors you created in earlier in this lesson.

Safety

Follow standard safety rules and school safety rules for laboratory activities.

Procedure

1. Collect all the index cards you placed around the school.

2. Use the balance to determine the mass of each index card.

3. Determine the difference in mass from the beginning of the experiment to its end.

4. Create a table to record and communicate your data.

Analysis Questions

1. Write a paragraph that describes the results of your experiment. Include data about where in your school you found the most and the fewest particulates.

2. Were you surprised by any of your results? If so, explain why.

3. How could you change the procedure of this experiment to collect even more particulates?

4. Answer the essential question: *How are particulates distributed around your school?*

Ash and Particulate Emissions

Essential Question: *How do ash and other small particle emissions move from the power plant into ecosystems?*

Overview

In this lesson, you will read about how coal-burning power plants produce ash and other airborne solid particles. You will also learn how the particles are dispersed in the environment.

Ash and Particulate Emissions

Burning carbon-based material produces ash. In coal-burning power plants, some ash goes up the smokestack and is released into the air. You have probably seen a long stream of smoke being dispersed from a smokestack. If so, you know that the ash and everything else that leaves the smokestack does not stay put. It is carried away by the wind.

There are two kinds of coal ash, fly ash and bottom ash. Fly ash is the product of combustion that rises up into the smokestack. Bottom ash is left in the boilers and combustion chambers in the power plant. The disposal of fly ash is an environmental challenge, but, in this reading we will focus on the environmental impacts of fly ash emissions.

When ash and other solid particles leave a smokestack, they are lifted into the air by the wind. These particles are very small and light. They may remain airborne for days or even weeks before they settle to the Earth's surface. Depending on wind direction and speed, ash and particulates may be dispersed over very large distances. Sometimes, they wind up many hundreds or even thousands of miles away from the source that generated them. Any place on the Earth may receive ash waste from coal-burning power plants that are far away.

Airborne particles are brought down to Earth by a process known as *atmospheric deposition*. Some airborne particles are heavy enough that gravity pulls them down to the Earth's surface. Other particles are so light that they can stay in the air indefinitely. They are only brought to Earth by mixing with rain, snow, or fog. This is called *wet deposition*. Other light particles may reach the ground by *dry deposition* when they are deposited with dry particles like dust.

In addition to wet and dry deposition, there are two other deposition processes, *direct* and *indirect* deposition. Direct deposition occurs locally when particles enter bodies of water directly from a power plant or other sources. Indirect deposition occurs when particulates that have fallen on the land are washed into bodies of water by rain.

The deposition of pollutants can seriously disrupt aquatic ecosystems and surrounding land ecosystems. Among the most harmful of the airborne pollutants deposited in water are heavy metals (lead, mercury, etc.) and nitrogen compounds. Heavy metals are toxic to animals. Nitrogen is essential for plant growth, but too much nitrogen can disrupt an aquatic ecosystem. Too much nitrogen in a body of water can cause an explosion of algae populations that will eventually deplete the oxygen that fish and other aquatic organisms require to live.

Another type of power plant pollutant that can be deposited in water is a class of highly toxic products of combustion that includes dioxins and furans. When deposited in water, they can cause deadly hormonal, reproductive, neurological, and immune system damage in animals. To make matters worse, these toxic compounds can persist in the environment for decades.

The problem of the deposition of airborne ash and particulates has become worldwide. Satellite images confirm that ash and soil dust pollution reach the U.S. after being blown across the oceans from Asia and Africa. European scientists have traced some of its pollution to coal-burning power plants in the U.S.

Modern coal-burning power plants use a variety of technologies to reduce the impact of pollution from ash. The way the function is to lower the level of toxics in power plant emissions and to capture ash before it leaves the smokestack.

Analysis Questions

1. Where in a power plant is the ash that leaves the smokestack produced?

2. What is deposition? Describe two kinds of deposition.

3. How are ash and particulates carried from the smokestack to areas hundreds of miles from the power plant?

4. Name three toxic compounds from coal-burning power plants that "hitch a ride" on airborne ash and particulates.

5. How do scientists know that the problem of airborne pollutants is global? What do you think should be done to reduce the effects of these pollutants in the U.S.?

6. Answer the essential question: *How do ash and other small particle emissions move from the power plant into ecosystems?*

Mercury Bioaccumulation

Essential Question: *How does mercury pollution affect loons living in Wisconsin lakes?*

Overview

In the previous lesson, you learned how particulate pollutants are produced and released by power plants. In this lesson, you will read about mercury and how it accumulates in wildlife. Mercury is a particularly harmful pollutant produced by coal-burning power plants.

Mercury Bioaccumulation and Wisconsin Loons

Mercury is a type of element known as a heavy metal. It can be found in low concentrations in nature. It is released into the atmosphere when volcanoes erupt and rocks erode. Mercury is also released by the combustion of fossil fuels, particularly coal. Almost all particulate mercury is caught by plant scrubbers in the flue. However, gaseous mercury can escape into the atmosphere. Gaseous mercury can travel great distances, hundreds or even thousands of miles . Eventually, the mercury mixes with rain or snow and is deposited on land or into lakes and oceans.

Any animal, including humans, that consumes mercury faces serious health problems. Mercury is a neurotoxin, a substance that severely damages the nervous system. Even at low concentrations, it can cause nerve diseases and birth defects in offspring.

Mercury affects ecosystems through a process called *bioaccumulation*. Because of its many lakes, the ecosystems in southeast Wisconsin are particularly vulnerable to mercury bioaccumulation. When mercury is deposited in a lake, bacteria that are found in shallow water or lake sediment take in the mercury toxin. These bacteria convert elemental mercury into methyl-mercury. Worms, which are sediment-dwelling animals, and insects ingest the methyl-mercury. Fish feed on these worms and other organisms that contain the toxin. As fish eat more and more of these organisms, they take in all the mercury contained within the organism they just ate plus any mercury they have ingested themselves. In this way, the fish eventually have much higher mercury content then their food did. Mercury builds up in predators because they consume large amounts of fish already high in mercury content. This is the process of bioaccumulation.

Therefore, the top predator in an ecosystem is the most vulnerable to mercury poisoning. In southeastern Wisconsin, the common loon, is one such predator. Loons nest on lakes and feed only on lake fish. A pair of loons will consume up to 600 perch and bluegills a year. Because they live 20 to 25 years, a loon can accumulate an enormous quantity of mercury over its lifetime. The effects of mercury poisoning can be catastrophic for loons. A Canadian study found that loons with mercury levels of as low as 3 ppm showed bizarre nesting behavior and greatly reduced reproduction. In most lakes in northern Wisconsin, loons have mercury levels of

4 ppm or more. The loons' strange behavior is probably due to nervous-system damage caused by mercury. Studies in Wisconsin reveal that loons with high levels of mercury in their bodies also hatch fewer eggs and raise fewer young. Female loons also pass on mercury to the embryos in their eggs. This causes embryos to die or young to be born with severe birth defects.

Based on other studies, scientists predict that loons could exhibit three main effects of high mercury levels in their bodies. The first is embryo mortality. Second, the young that do hatch could suffer long-term health effects, particularly neurological and reproductive damage. Third, adult loons could show abnormal reproductive behavior. For example, loons may not properly incubate their eggs. They also may build a nest in one place, but lay eggs somewhere else.

Loons are not the only animals in their habitat that are affected by mercury. Many animals feed on mercury-contaminated fish found in Wisconsin lakes. Biologists compared mercury levels in loons to other fish-eating wildlife such as bald eagles, ospreys, mink, and otters. Loons showed the highest mercury concentrations among fish-eating wildlife. Fish-eaters in general showed higher mercury levels than herbivores and other carnivores.

Biologists in Wisconsin are conducting a long-range study to try to save Wisconsin's only species of loon. Researchers will try to establish a population model that predicts how mercury in fish will affect Wisconsin's common loon population. They will also study adult survival rate, the proportion of adults that breed, the number of young produced annually, and what proportion of those young survive to breed. Some studies will look at other toxic effects of mercury on loons. They will study the birds' reproductive performance, physiology, genetic material, immune and nervous systems, survival, and behavior. Loons will continue to be tested to monitor the mercury levels in their bodies.

Freshwater fish and their predators are not the only animals affected by mercury. Scientists have also found evidence of mercury bioaccumulation in predator fish in the oceans. One example is tuna, which is a large, long-lived ocean predator. Scientists have found steadily rising levels of mercury in the tissues of tuna over the years. In fact, the mercury levels in one type of tuna, albacore, have gotten so high that in 2004 the U.S. Environmental Protection Agency issued an advisory recommending that pregnant women and young children not eat more than one serving of albacore tuna a week. While this particular advisory only applies to one species of tuna, it shows how the impact of a human activity like electricity generation can cascade through the environment, eventually resulting in an impact on humans. In this case, humans are affected by the link between natural ecosystems and our food supply.

Analysis Questions

1. How does mercury get into the Wisconsin's lakes?

2. In what form is mercury taken up by fish? How is elemental mercury converted to this form?

3. How does methyl-mercury accumulate in the bodies of loons and other fish-eating predators?

4. Answer the essential question: *How does mercury pollution affect loons living in Wisconsin lakes?*

Lesson 3

Acidic Deposition and Smog

Driving Question: What are the impacts of the emissions from power plants?

Overview

In this chapter so far, you have learned about different types of emissions produced by coal-burning power plants. These emissions include gases and solid particulates. You have also learned how emissions find their way from the atmosphere to the Earth's surface through deposition processes. This lesson looks at the effects of deposition of sulfuric acid formed by SO_2 and nitric acid formed by NO_x. Acid deposition can be wet or dry with many of the same effects. Wet acidic deposition is called acid rain. Dry deposition occurs as the naturally "sticky" acid molecules attach themselves to objects like buildings or plants and leave the atmosphere. You will start this lesson with two lab activities. You will create acid rain yourself and see its effects on human-made materials. You will also read about the effects of acidic deposition on ecosystems. Finally, you will read about the smog that results from NO_x emissions and its impact on large cities across the country.

Important Content

- Burning coal forms unintended byproducts. These include carbon dioxide, nitrogen oxides, and sulfur dioxide.

- Gas emissions from power plants result in acidic deposition, pollution, and smog.

Creating Acid Rain

? *Essential Question: Compare your results in this lab to what happens to power plant emissions in the atmosphere.*

Overview

In the last several lessons, you have learned about the products of coal combustion. You have learned the way that ash and other particulates find their way into water supplies and ecosystems. SO_2 and NO_x affect the environment in very different ways. They chemically react with compounds in the atmosphere. Both SO_2 and NO_x are oxidized. SO_2 forms sulfuric acid and NO_x forms nitric acid when oxidized and mixed with water. When this happens in the atmosphere, the precipitation that results is know as acid rain. In this activity, you will observe the change in pH when water is exposed to combustion products. You will then compare this to what occurs in the atmosphere.

Materials

universal indicator solution (or another acid/base indicator)
samples of acids and bases (lemon juice, bleach)
graduated cylinder
distilled water
matches
eyedropper
plastic zip-lock bag (sandwich size)
clear plastic cups

Safety

Wear your goggles and lab apron. Follow standard safety rules for using glassware or working with matches. Tie back long hair, and tie back or remove any article of clothing or jewelry that can hang down and touch chemicals or flames.

Procedure

1. First, test your indicator solution (or pH paper) with known substances that are acidic, neutral and basic. Complete the following chart by testing lemon juice, distilled water, and bleach with the indicator solution.

If substance is...	Indicator color is...
Acidic	
Neutral	
Basic	

2. Place 5 mL of distilled water in the zip-lock bag. Seal the bag. Swirl the water around inside the bag until the entire inside is covered with droplets. Pour the excess water out of the bag.

3. **For this next step, be sure the follow the safety instructions given by your teacher.** Carefully light a kitchen match and set a piece of paper towel on fire. Quickly blow out both flames and collect as much smoke as possible in the bag. Seal the bag immediately.

4. Pour 5 mL of distilled water into the bag, being careful not to let any of the smoke out. Seal the bag quickly and swirl the water inside the bag again.

5. Put 2 drops of indicator solution into a cup.

6. Slowly open the bag and pour the water from the bag into the cup with the indicator. Record your observations.

Analysis Questions

1. Based on your observations, does the water become acidic, neutral or basic when smoke mixes with it?

2. Complete an input output diagram for this reaction.

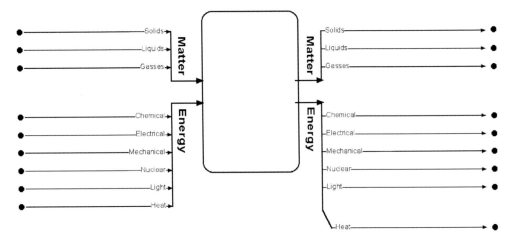

3. Answer the essential question: *Compare your results in this lab to what happens to power plant emissions in the atmosphere.*

Basics of Acid Deposition

Essential Question: List three ways that acidic deposition could affect lakes in Wisconsin.

Basics of Acidic Deposition

Acidic deposition is a widespread problem. In the U.S., most acidic deposition damage has occurred in the forests of the northeast. Some of the acidic rain that falls on the northeast is caused by coal-burning power plants in the midwest. In North America, weather generally travels from west to east. Sulfur dioxide and nitrogen oxides emitted by power plants in the midwest mix with water in the atmosphere and form clouds that are carried to the east. For example, emissions from power plants in Ohio and western Pennsylvania can result in acidic rain and dry acidic deposition that fall on forests in New York and New Hampshire.

Acidic Deposition in Lakes and Streams

A stream or lake's normal pH is between 6 and 8. When acidic deposition falls on these bodies of water, their pH can drop to 4 or even lower. These are conditions that can kill fish and other aquatic life. However, all animals are not affected the same way by acidic deposition. Some can survive a large change in acidity, while others are affected by even the smallest changes.

As lakes and streams become more acidic, some of the fish and other aquatic organisms that live in these waters die. At pH 5, most fish eggs cannot hatch. As pH becomes even more acidic, some adult fish die as well. It is possible for the entire fish population in a lake to die off as a result of acidic deposition. The chart below shows the range of pH that different freshwater organisms can tolerate. Lower pH values (more acidic water) will lower their chances of survival.

	pH 6.5	pH 6.0	pH 5.5	pH 5.0	pH 4.5	pH 4.0
Trout						
Bass						
Perch						
Frogs						
Salamanders						
Clams						
Crayfish						
Snails						
Mayfly						

As you learned in Unit 1, the plants and animals living within the same ecosystem are interdependent. So, if acidity affects one species, then organisms that rely on that species for food will be affected as well. For example, frogs can tolerate fairly high levels of acidity. However, mayflies, one of their primary food sources, are very intolerant of acidity. Thus, frog populations may be affected by acid deposition, even though they can tolerate the acid water themselves. If acidic deposition causes the loss of certain plant and animal species, the fish that rely on these organisms for food may also be affected. Populations of birds and other animals that are farther up the food chain that feed on the fish may also be affected.

The effect of acid deposition on a lake or pond depends in part on how large its watershed is. A watershed is the area of land that drains into a particular body of water. The larger the watershed is, the more acid water will reach the lake or pond.

The effect of acid deposition on a lake or pond also depends on the ability of the soils in the watershed to neutralize the acid. Substances called "buffers" react chemically with acids to make them less acidic. Some minerals commonly found in soils, like limestone, act as buffers. They react with the acidic water is it passes over or through the soil. This reaction to these minerals tend to reduce the water's acidity. The ability of soil to neutralize acid is called its "buffering capacity." The buffering capacity of the soil in a watershed determines the effect of acid rain. In an area with high buffering capacity, acid rain will have less of an effect on the pH of the lakes or ponds. In an area with low buffering capacity, the acid rain will have more effect on the pH of the lakes or ponds. However, as the buffer in soil reacts with acid, it looses its ability to neutralize acid. So, over long periods of exposure to acid, the buffering capacity of the soil declines.

Areas with a low buffering capacity suffer from another problem. Acidic deposition also causes aluminum from the soil to be released into lakes and streams. Aluminum is very toxic to many species of aquatic organisms. It often affects fishes' gills, which become encrusted and eventually sealed. These fish die from slow suffocation, as their gills can no longer take in oxygen from the water.

The Effect of Acidic Deposition on Trees and Plants

Acidic deposition is also harmful to trees and plants on land. Acidic deposition weakens trees by limiting the soil nutrients available to them. Scientists believe that acidic water dissolves valuable nutrients and minerals in the soil. It then washes them away before the trees and other plants can use them to grow. Acidic deposition also causes the release of toxic substances, like aluminum, into the soil. Even limited amounts of these toxins are very harmful to trees and plants. These toxins are present in minerals in soil and are usually released in very small quantities as neutral water passes through the soil. Acidic water causes them to be released in much larger quantities.

Forests in high mountain regions receive additional acid from the acidic clouds and fog that often surround them. These clouds and fog are often more acidic than rainfall. When leaves are bathed in this acid fog, their protective waxy coating can dissolve. The loss of this coating damages the leaves and creates brown spots. When leaves are damaged, they cannot produce enough energy for the tree to remain healthy. Once trees are weak, they are more easily attacked by diseases or insects that eventually kill them. Weakened trees may also become damaged more easily by cold weather.

Acidic deposition harms other plants the same way it harms trees. Food crops are not usually seriously affected, however, because farmers add fertilizers to the soil to replace lost nutrients. They may also add crushed limestone to the soil. Limestone is basic and helps protect the soil against acidity.

For years, scientists and foresters saw forests grow abnormally slowly without knowing why. They saw trees' leaves and needles turn brown and fall off when they should have been green and healthy. In extreme cases, entire areas of the forest simply died off, without an obvious reason.

Researchers now know that acidic deposition causes slower growth, injury, or death of forests. Acidic deposition has been blamed for forest and soil destruction in many areas of the eastern U.S., The areas hit the hardest are the high-elevation forests of the Appalachian Mountains from Maine to Georgia. Acidic deposition has damaged areas in the Adirondacks, the Shenandoah, and Great Smoky Mountains. Acidic deposition is not the only cause of such conditions. Other factors like insect infestation, disease, drought, or very cold weather also harm trees and plants. In fact, the impacts of acidic deposition on trees usually occur in combination with these other environmental factors. Scientists have spent many years studying the chemistry and biology of forests. They are beginning to understand how acidic deposition affects the forest soil, trees, and other plants.

Analysis Questions

1. How does acid precipitation affect aquatic animals? Describe how the interdependence of animals and plants in a lake ecosystem increases the effects of acidic deposition throughout the ecosystem.

2. How does acidic deposition affect trees and forests? Why does it inhibit growth? How does it make trees more prone to other conditions that might kill them?

3. Why are high-elevation forests more severely affected by acidic deposition than those at lower altitudes?

4. Answer the essential question: *List three ways that acidic deposition could affect lakes in Wisconsin.*

Effects on Buildings

Essential Question: *What materials should architects consider using for buildings in areas affected by acid rain?*

Overview

As you learned in the last reading, acid rain affects animal and plant life. It also affects the buildings where we live and work. It contributes to the corrosion of metals such as bronze. It contributes to the deterioration of paint. It also contributes to the erosion of stone such as marble and limestone. These effects damage buildings, bridges, statues, monuments, tombstones, and cars. Some U.S. car manufacturers use acid-resistant paints to reduce the damage caused by acid rain. This costs an average of $5 for each new vehicle or $61 million per year. In this lab, you will look at the effects of acid rain on building materials, including limestone and metal.

Materials

5% acetic acid solution
eye dropper
limestone and other building materials
steel wool
plastic cups
vinegar
pH paper
universal indicator
distilled water

Safety

Follow standard safety rules and school safety rules for laboratory activities.

Procedure:

Part A: Indicators

1. Create a table to record the pH and the color with universal indicator for vinegar, 5% acetic acid, and distilled water.

2. Test the pH of water, 5% acetic acid and vinegar with separate pieces of pH paper. Record the pH of all substances in your table.

3. Test the water, 5% acetic acid and vinegar with universal indicator. Record the color of the indicator in your table.

Part B: Building Materials

1. Create 2 tables with the following as column headers. The first table should be labeled "Materials in Water" and the second "Materials in Acid."

2. Each group will be assigned a building material for all observations, massing, and preparation.

Material	Initial description	Initial mass	Initial pH	Day 2 pH and description	Day 3 pH and description	Day 4 pH	Day 4 description	Day 4 mass (after drying)

3. Take 2 pieces of your assigned building material and take the mass of each.

4. Write the mass and physical observations in the correct box on your tables. Keep track of which sample you plan to put in acid, and which in water.

5. Place each rock in a small beaker. One beaker should be filled with enough acetic acid to cover the building sample. The other should be filled with enough distilled water to cover the building sample.

6. Take the initial pH of both beakers and observe for any immediate changes.

7. Fill in all your information on the table. Be prepared to share the data with the class.

8. On Day 2 and Day 3, take the pH and record all observations in the correct table. Share the data with your classmates

9. After you observe and take the pH on Day 4, dispose of the liquid according to your teacher's instructions. Rinse your sample. Place on a watch glass that is labeled (acid or water) and let it dry.

10. When the sample is dry, take the mass and record the results.

Part C: Metal

1. Create a table to record your results from Part C. The table should be similar to your table from Part B

2. Put 2 samples of steel wool in 2 separate 50 mL beakers. Label the first "distilled water" and the second "vinegar."

3. Fill the distilled beaker with enough distilled water to cover the steel wool.

4. Fill the vinegar beaker with enough vinegar to cover the steel wool.

5. Place in the hood overnight.

Analysis Questions

1. How much mass did each sample of building materials gain/lose over the last few days?

2. Which of these building materials would be the best to use for a building in a city with an acid rain problem? Justify your answer with your results.

3. Describe in detail the changes in the steel wool in both distilled water and in the vinegar.

4. Think about the metal objects that are exposed to water and harsh chemicals everyday. How are they protected from being damaged like the steel wool in this experiment?

5. Answer the essential question: *What materials should architects consider using for buildings in areas affected by acid rain?*

Smog

Essential Questions: *What is smog and how does it form? What are smog's effects on people?*

What is Smog?

The brown haze that often hangs over large American cities, usually in summer, is commonly known as smog. Technically, it's called photochemical smog because sunlight is necessary for its formation.

Smog forms when three ingredients combine: nitrogen oxides (NO_x), volatile organic compounds (VOCs), and energy from the Sun in the form of ultraviolet (UV) rays. In big cities, the primary sources of nitrogen oxides and volatile organic compounds are diesel vehicles, gasoline vehicles, and coal-burning power plants. Though coal-burning power plants contribute to smog, the worst smog conditions are usually the result of vehicle emissions during the summer. The heat, intense sunlight, and large numbers of cars are on the roads around cities during the summer create ideal conditions for smog to form.

The two main components of smog are nitrogen dioxide (NO_2) and ozone (O_3). As you learned earlier, both nitric oxide (NO) and nitrogen dioxide (NO_2) are present in emissions from coal-burning power plants. They are also found in the emissions of motor vehicles. Nitrogen dioxide is a yellow-brown gas with a powerful, choking odor. It is one of the ingredients that give smog its distinctive color and smell.

Volatile organic chemicals (VOCs) play an important role in the conversion of NO to NO_2 in the formation of smog. Volatile organic compounds are hydrocarbons, molecules made up mostly of carbon and hydrogen. VOCs are emitted when fossil fuels are not completely burned. They are present in vehicle emissions and, to a lesser extent, in the emissions of coal power plants. VOCs also come from chemical plants, oil refineries, and other industrial plants, as well as a wide variety of natural sources including trees. When volatile organic compounds react with oxygen (O_2) in the atmosphere, they start a chain of reactions that convert nitric oxide into nitrogen dioxide (NO_2).

Nitrogen dioxide is an important ingredient of smog, but it also contributes to the formation of ozone, the other major ingredient. When the UV rays in sunlight hit a nitrogen dioxide molecule, the nitrogen dioxide splits to form nitric oxide plus an atom of oxygen:

$$NO_2 + UV \text{ energy} \rightarrow NO + O$$

The single atoms of oxygen (O) produced through this reaction then bond with molecules of oxygen gas (O_2) to form ozone:

$$O + O_2 \rightarrow O_3$$

Ozone is an invisible gas that has a sharp, acidic smell and taste. The ozone that forms through this process is called *ground-level* or *tropospheric* ozone because it occurs in the troposphere, the bottom layer of the atmosphere. When ozone occurs at ground-level, it irritates the breathing passages of animals, including humans, and can cause serious damage to lungs. People with asthma, heart disease, or other health problems that impair breathing are particularly vulnerable to ozone. Many cities in the United States experience ozone alert days during the summer. During those days, the government advises healthy people to avoid exercise and elderly people or people with respiratory problems to avoid any outdoor activity altogether.

It is important to understand the difference between this ground-level ozone that is created as a result of human activity and the stratospheric ozone layer that occurs naturally higher up in the atmosphere. The stratosphere is the layer of the atmosphere that occurs above the troposphere. The ozone layer in the stratosphere has concentrations of ozone that are more than one hundred fifty times the concentrations measured in ground-level smog. The stratospheric ozone layer protects life on Earth by absorbing potentially harmful ultraviolet rays from the sun. Stratospheric ozone is considered good because it prevents plants and animals from being harmed by exposure to too much ultraviolet energy. On the other hand, ground-level ozone is considered bad because it is an irritant to plants and animals.

Ground-level ozone is not the only harmful product that results from reactions between volatile organic chemicals and oxygen. The same kinds of reactions that produce ozone also produce peroxyacetyl nitrates (PANs) and (PAHs) polycyclic aromatic hydrocarbons, which have irritating effects that are similar to ground-level ozone. Like NO_2, PANs are brown and contribute to smog's brown, hazy color.

While motor vehicles are the primary source of the emissions that contribute to smog in the U.S., coal-burning power plants have been major emitters of NO_x historically. Thus, cities near coal-burning power plants have experienced frequent and serious episodes of smog. Even in areas without large numbers of motor vehicles, there can be high enough levels of VOCs in the atmosphere from natural emitters like trees to create smog. For example, scientists have determined that smog that occurs in rural areas of the southeast U.S. is the result of NOx emissions from coal power plants mixing with VOCs emitted by oak trees in large forested areas.

Because nitrogen oxides are released when coal is burned at high temperatures, coal power plant engineers have developed technologies for reducing NO_x emissions by lowering the combustion temperature in boilers. According to the Coalition for Affordable and Reliable Energy, an industry organization that includes power companies, by 2004 these low NO_x burner technologies had been installed or were being installed on 75% of the coal power plants in the U.S.

Analysis Questions

1. What role do nitrogen gases have in the formation of smog? Where do these gases come from?

2. Where does the energy necessary for smog formation come from?

3. How do coal-burning power plants contribute to smog?

4. Answer the essential questions: *What is smog and how does it form? What are smog's effects on people?*

Lesson 4
Water Impacts

Driving Question: *How is the water in the reservoir affected by a power plant?*

Overview

Fossil fuel power plants use water in two ways. First, they use water to make steam to turn the turbine. They also use water to cool the steam after it has passed through the turbine and turn the steam back into liquid water. In this lesson, you will look at what happens to that water after it has been used. Some of the water enters the atmosphere through evaporation, and, some of the water is returned to its source near the power plant. This lesson focuses on the environmental effects of this water use. Ecosystems are sensitive to change, so you will explore how animals and plants in a lake might be affected by the use of that lake's water in a power plant. In the first activity, you will calculate the amount of water used by a coal-burning power plant. You will then read about how water is changed when it passes through a power plant and the effects of returning that water to its source.

Important Content

- Power plants can have serious impacts on the bodies of water that they get their water from. This is because of the withdrawal of water and because of the temperature difference in the water that is returned.

- Power plants use water to generate steam within the power plant. They also use it for cooling that steam before it is released.

Water Use by Power Plants

Essential Question: How much water that a coal-burning power plant takes from a supply lake is not returned to the lake?

Overview

In this activity, you will determine how much water a coal-burning power plant requires. With your class, you will trace the water in a power plant from the lake that supplies the water to the boiler to steam, and then back to the lake. At each step, you will be asked to keep track of how much water you have and how much water is lost. In the end, you will know the total amount of water needed and used by this power plant.

Procedure

A typical 350 MW power plant requires 0.9 m^3 of water per second. This water is pumped from the lake to the boiler. In the boiler, the boiling water becomes steam, which turns the turbine to generate electricity. From there, the steam is sent to a cooling tower or pond where it cools and condenses to liquid water again. However, during this process, water is "lost" through evaporation at a rate of about 0.6 m^3 per second. This lost water enters the atmosphere. The remaining water (0.3 m^3 per second) is returned to the lake.

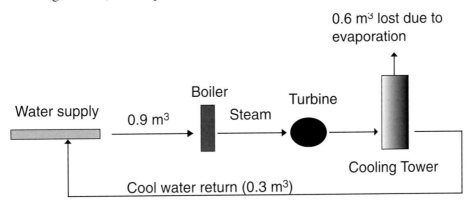

Scientists call the portion of the water that is not returned to the lake the water that is consumed. Using the figure of 0.6 m^3 of water consumed per second from above, we can calculate how much water is consumed by a power plant in a day and in six months (180 days).

$$\frac{0.6 \text{ m}^3}{s} \times \frac{86,400 s}{day} \qquad \frac{\text{m}^3}{day}$$

$$\frac{\text{m}^3}{day}$$

This calculation tells us that the power plant consumes 5.18×10^4 (51,800) m^3 of water a day and 9.33×10^6 (9,330,000) m^3 of water in 180 days. So the power plant's lake must be larger than this. The general rule that scientists and engineers use for calculating how big a lake must be is: the power plant should not use more than 72% of the lake's total volume of water every 6 months. Since a lake is always being refilled by precipitation and the streams and rivers that feed it, this does not mean that the lake's level will drop by 72% every six months. In fact, this amount is calculated to maintain a reasonable water level in the lake.

$$9.33 \times 10^6 \text{ m}^3 \times \frac{100\% \text{ total lake volume}}{72\% \text{ for power plant}} = 1.30 \times 10^7 \text{ m}^3$$

Using the figure of 72%, we can determine how big a lake must be in order to meet this requirement.

This calculation tells us that a lake must have a total volume of at least 1.30×10^7 (13,000,000) m^3 to supply enough water for a 350 MW power plant.

How big a lake is that? The answer depends on the depth. A lake whose depth averages 400 meters would have to have an area equal to 12 football fields. A lake whose average depth is only 5 meters would have to have the same area as a square one 1 mile long and one mile wide.

Analysis Questions

1. A coal-burning power plant pulls in 0.9 m^3 of water each second. How much water is this each hour? Each day? Compare this amount to an everyday object. Is this enough water to fill a kitchen sink? A swimming pool?

2. Imagine this quantity of water being sucked out of a lake. What do you think might happen to fish or small creatures that are near the water intake valve of the power plant?

3. The size of a lake needed to support the power plant is quite large. Are there any lakes in close to where you live that are large enough to supply the water for a coal-burning power plant?

4. Answer the essential question: *How much water that a coal-burning power plant takes from a supply lake is not returned to the lake?* Give your answer for the period of a day, month, and year.

Impacts of Water Use

 Essential Question: *How does water use in power plants affect the water source?*

Overview

Coal-burning power plants use water in several ways. They get their water from a lake or river near the plant site. In this lesson, you will read about how water use by power plants affects the temperature of the water they withdraw from lakes or other sources.

How do power plants use and consume water?

To review how coal-burning power plants use water, they generate electricity by heating water and turning it into steam that drives turbines. The steam is cooled and condenses back into water. This water is then mixed with fresh water and reheated to drive the turbines again. A separate supply of cool water is used to absorb the heat of the steam and cool it down until it condenses back into liquid water. Condenser systems usually consist of thousands of one-inch-diameter tubes. Cooling water is run through the tubes, and the hot steam and water circulates over them.

There are currently two cooling technologies in use:

- *Once-through* systems require cooling water from a source with a continual flow. The water demand for the once-through system is 30 to 50 times that of a closed cycle system.

- *Closed-cycle* systems recycle water within the power plant. Less water is required for this system. Closed-cycle systems are also expensive.

Once-through systems are much more common in the United States because of their lower cost and because water is generally plentiful.

The amount of water a power plant uses for cooling varies according to the plant's technology and size. Together all the steam-driven power plants in the U.S. withdraw more than 200 billion gallons of water per day from lakes and rivers. This is about half of all withdrawals from surface water in the country.

A power plant's *water use* is a measure of the amount of water it withdraws from a water source. Because some of the water is returned to the source, there are environmental impacts of power plant water use. These impacts are caused by chemical or physical changes to the water. These changes may have an impact on the ecosystem that includes the water source. The coal-burning power plant in Wisconsin that you will help determine the site of uses 0.9 m^3 of water per second. Of that, .3 m^3 per second will be returned to its source after being used in the plant.

A power plant's *water consumption* is water that is not returned to the source, usually because of evaporation. The primary concern with water consumption is that it is no longer available to support the ecosystem it was withdrawn from, or for other human uses. The coal-burning power plant in Wisconsin that you will help determine the site of has a water consumption rate of 0.6 m^3 of water per second.

The consequences of water use and consumption

The withdrawal of large volumes of water from natural waterways for power plants can kill fish, fish larvae, and other organisms. These creatures often become trapped against the plant's intake valves. They can also be swept up in the water flow through different sections of the plant. Because of the large volume of water required by power plants and the large demand for electricity in the U.S. these impacts can add up. For example, in 2004, there were 90 power plants using *once-through-cooling* on the Great Lakes. Scientists have estimated that more than 40 million fish per year die by being caught in the intake systems of these plants.

Another impact of water use is *thermal pollution*, or pollution caused by heat   Thermal pollution occurs because power plants typically return water that is warmer than it was when it was withdrawn. Adding large quantities of heated water to a lake will raise the lake's overall temperature, which can have a dramatic effect on the lake's ecosystem.

Water temperature directly affects the health and physiology of fish. Most fish are very sensitive to the temperature of the water where they live. Some fish can tolerate only very narrow variations in water temperature. Fish are "cold blooded" animals. Their internal body temperature depends on the external temperature–the water temperature. Fish are able to be active and feed only at certain temperatures. These temperatures vary by species. The ability of fish to digest food depends on water temperature remaining within a limited range.

Water temperature also affects fish reproduction. Each species of fish has a narrow temperature range within which they will reproduce and their eggs will survive and hatch. Water temperature also affects embryo development. Embryos inside fish eggs will die if the water temperature is not within an acceptable range. Hatchlings will not survive temperatures outside this range. Most power plants are located on the shallow shores of water bodies where spawning and hatching occur. Discharging warm water into these environments can have a devastating effect on fish reproduction and fish populations.

There is also a connection between water temperature and the amount of dissolved oxygen in the water. The amount of oxygen in water affects the life it can support. The warmer the water, the less dissolved oxygen it can hold. Some fish, such as trout, need cold water with high levels of dissolved oxygen. They cannot live in warmer water. Other fish, such as carp, thrive in warmer water with less dissolved oxygen. When thermal pollution from power plants warms lake water, some cold-water fish species cannot survive because they cannot breathe. Other fish species may take over habitats from cold-water fish if waters become too warm. The effects of these changes in fish populations can spread through the food web to organisms that eat or are eaten by the species that are directly affected.

Warmer water can also reduce the level of dissolved oxygen in water through a dramatic growth of algae called an "algae bloom." Warm water provides a better environment for certain types of freshwater algae (tiny water plants) to grow. The algae thrive in warm water and their populations can grow rapidly. However, algae are short-lived. When they die, they sink to the lake bottom where they decompose. This decomposition uses up a great deal of dissolved oxygen, leaving even less in the water for fish to breathe. Some species of algae also produce toxins that are deadly to fish or other aquatic organisms. Widespread deaths of aquatic organisms often result from these algae blooms.

Thermal pollution has become a recognized problem in many places. However, the technology to prevent it is relatively simple. Most states have passed laws requiring power plants to cool waste water before releasing it back into lakes or streams. Power plants can keep their waste water in cooling facilities until has cooled enough to be safely discharged back into the water body. While this is an effective way to reduce the impact of energy generation on the environment, it does add to the cost of generating the energy.

Analysis Questions

1. Why do power plants need so much water? What is it used for?

2. How is the water discharged by a power plant different from when that water was withdrawn for use?

3. How are fish affected by changes in water temperature? Why are they so sensitive to temperature?

4. How does water temperature affect the amount of oxygen the water can hold? How does thermal pollution by power plants affect the level of dissolved oxygen in water?

5. What effect does thermal pollution by power plants have on algae? How does the growth of algae populations affect fish?

6. Answer the essential question: *How does water use in power plants affect the water source?*

Ecosystem Impacts

Essential Question: *What changes might you see in the ecosystem because of increased water use and increased water temperature?*

Overview

In the previous activity, you read about how power plants affect lakes. You learned how their withdrawal and warming of water affects lake ecosystems.

In this lesson, you will analyze a table that shows the best water temperatures for some species of northern fish during different parts of their life cycle. The table also shows the minimum amount of oxygen that must be dissolved in water for fish to be able to breathe. As you study the table, remember the amount of water power plants withdraw from a lake every second of every day. Recall from Lesson 4: *Water Use by Power Plants* that the water a power plant returns to the lake is as much as 10°F warmer than the water it withdrew.

Procedure

Use the following information to answer the analysis questions.

Temperature (°F) and dissolved oxygen (mg/L) requirements for some northern freshwater fish species

Fish	Living Temp	Upper Lethal Temp.	Spawning Temp.	Juvenile Growth Temp.
Chinook Salmon	57-68*	77.4	42-57	45-58
Coho Salmon	45-60	78.4	39.9-48.9	53.2-58.3
Steelhead Trout	n/a	75.4	39-48.9	45.1-58.3
Brown Trout	n/a	75.4	45-55	39-70.3
Largemouth Bass	65-80	95	70**	90**
Northern Pike	56-74	88	40-45	n/a
Walleye	64-78	84.2	42-50	n/a
Yellow Perch	63.8-82.5	84	n/a	n/a
Muskelunge	33-78	90	55	n/a

* summer temperature

**maximum temperature

Average Seasonal Water Temperatures for Lake Geneva, Wisconsin

July	74°F (surface)
	65°F (bottom)
August	82°F (surface)
	70°F (bottom)
October	52°F (surface)
	47°F (bottom)
December	0°F (frozen surface)
	39°F (bottom)
March	50°F (surface)
	45°F (bottom)

Analysis Questions

1. Which adult fish would probably be best able to survive increased water temperature?

2. In an earlier lesson, you looked at the effects of acid rain on the aquatic food web. Are the same organisms going to be affected by warmer water as are affected by acid rain?

3. Study the water temperatures for Lake Geneva above. Which fish species would be unable to survive if a power plant discharges increased the water temperature in spring and summer by 10°F?

4. Suppose power plant discharge raised the water temperature in Lake Geneva by 10°F. Which fish species would be affected by a water temperature that had reached their upper lethal limit?

5. Looking at the aquatic food web for Wisconsin lakes, answer the essential question: *What changes might you see in the ecosystem because of increased water use and increased water temperature?*

Lesson 5
Dispersion of Impacts

 Driving Question: *How far can the environmental impacts of a power plant spread?*

Overview

This lesson covers the ways that impacts from coal-burning power plants spread over large distances. You will consider the statement, "Dilution is the solution to pollution" and decide if you agree with it. You will start with an activity that shows how smokestacks are used to reduce the concentration of pollutants. You'll learn how airborne pollution spreads in plumes and about the layers of the atmosphere. By the end of the lesson, you will put all of this information into a diagram. The diagram will show how widespread the impacts of the coal-burning power plant will be. This will help you prepare for the next chapter, where you will make a decision about where to locate a coal-burning power plant. The plant's impacts will be a major part of that decision.

Important Content

*   Because of wind and air movement in the atmosphere, local pollution problems can spread over large areas.

*   The area affected by a power plant extends beyond the area immediately surrounding the power plant. In fact, a single power plant can impact areas that are hundreds of miles away.

Smokestacks

Essential Question: Why do power plants have tall smokestacks?

Overview

In earlier lessons, you learned about atmospheric pollutants and how they are formed and released by coal-burning power plants. You have also learned about some of the ways that power plants can reduce their emissions.

In this lesson, you will look at where and how those pollutants spread. Later, you will predict what the effects of building a new power plant might be. In this activity, you will use sand to represent emissions from a coal-burning power plant. You will compare the distances the sand spreads depending on the elevation from which it is released.

Materials

1 large sheet of white paper (3' x 4' or larger)
clear tape
2 tablespoons sand
old textbooks

Procedure

1. Tape the large sheet of paper to the tabletop. In the corner of the paper farthest from the edge, draw an "X" 2 cm from each side of the paper. (See diagram on the next page.)

2. Place one small spoonful of sand on the X.

3. Gently blow the sand as shown in the diagram. On the paper, draw a loop around the area where the sand has spread.

4. Clean all the sand off of the paper.

5. Stack the textbooks so they tower over the X. Place one spoonful atop the books. This spoonful of sand should be in the same location as the previous one, only higher.

6. Gently blow the sand again. Draw a loop around the area where the sand has spread.

7. Clean up all your materials.

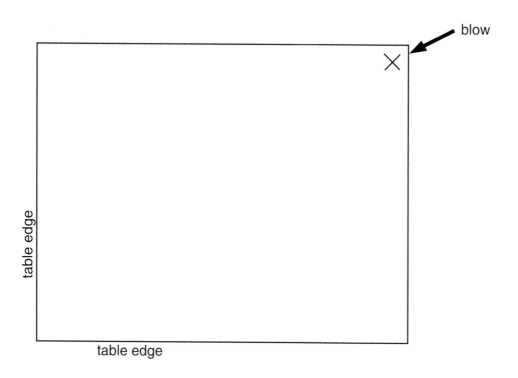

Figure 1: Laboratory Setup. Not to scale.

Analysis Questions

1. Describe the difference between the two loops. Which one covers a larger area? Which one had more sand? The concentration of a pollutant is the amount of pollutant found in a fixed space. Which loop had a higher concentration of sand?

2. Smokestacks are intended to spread pollution out over a larger area so that the concentration of pollution in the air is not high enough in any one place to cause adverse effects. Does this seem like a good solution to the problem of power plant emissions? Why or why not?

3. Answer the essential question: *Why do power plants have tall smokestacks?*

Layers of Atmosphere

Essential Question: *What are the major differences between the troposphere, stratosphere, and mesosphere?*

Overview

In this activity, you will learn about the layers of the Earth's atmosphere. This background information will help you to understand how emissions are spread.

Composition of the Atmosphere

Earth's atmosphere is like an ocean of air that surrounds the planet. Compared to the diameter of the Earth, the atmosphere is very shallow. Compared the size of living things on Earth, or even the deepest oceans and tallest mountains, the atmosphere is very deep. The Earth's present-day atmosphere has a different composition than long ago. Our current atmosphere is called an oxidizing atmosphere – an atmosphere rich in oxygen. The original atmosphere had no free oxygen (O_2) at all. Most of the oxygen in our atmosphere was produced billions of years ago by tiny coastal bacteria called stomatolites. The stomatolites converted the carbon dioxide in the atmosphere into oxygen through photosynthesis, which is the way plants convert solar energy to chemical energy that they can use to grow. Over billions of years, the oxygen given off by stomatolites accumulated in the atmosphere. Today's atmosphere is made up of about 78% nitrogen, 21% oxygen, and small amounts of many other gases.

Layers of the Atmosphere

The atmosphere of the Earth is divided into four layers, the troposphere, stratosphere, mesosphere, and thermosphere. Each has its own distinct characteristics. The boundaries between these layers are named the tropopause (between the troposphere and stratosphere), stratopause (between the stratosphere and mesosphere), mesopause (between the methosphere and thermosphere).

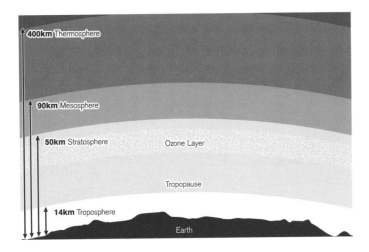

The Troposphere

The troposphere is the layer of the atmosphere closest to the surface of the Earth. The troposphere extends from the Earth's surface to an altitude of about 18 km at the equator and 8 km at the Poles. The troposphere contains 80% of the total mass of the atmosphere and almost all of the water vapor. The troposphere's vertical temperature range from warmest near the surface to coldest at the tropopause is about 6.5°C per kilometer. The troposphere is where the majority of clouds are formed and most weather occurs. The troposphere is where air masses move and collide, resulting in Earth's daily weather patterns. It's also the layer that air currents, like the jet stream over North America, flow through.

The Stratosphere and Ozone Layer

Extending from the tropopause to about 50 km is the stratosphere. Compared to the troposphere, the stratosphere is dry, stable, has little movement of air masses, and is rich in ozone. About 90% of the ozone in the atmosphere is in the stratosphere. The air temperatures remain constant up to 20 km and then increase with altitude up to 50 km. The warmth is due primarily to absorption of ultraviolet (UV) radiation in the ozone layer in the upper stratosphere. The ozone layer has the highest concentrations of ozone near 25 km in the tropical region and about 20 km in the Polar Regions. Ozone is a very reactive molecule that consists of three oxygen atoms. Ozone in the stratosphere is 'good' ozone. It absorbs most of the ultraviolet (UV) radiation that reaches the Earth from the Sun. The ozone layer thus protects all Earth's organisms from the extremely harmful effects of UV radiation.

About 60 years ago, chlorofluorocarbons (CFCs), were invented to use in refrigerators and air conditioners. They were also used in the manufacture of various materials such as solvents and insulating foams. CFCs are all very stable molecules, which means they do not react easily with other chemicals, so they do not break down in the atmosphere. When released into the air, these CFCs rise into the stratosphere and the ozone layer. Only the powerful UV rays in the stratosphere are able to break down these molecules. When CFCs do break down, these chemicals release free atoms of chlorine. The free atoms break apart molecules of ozone in the ozone layer. In the presence of sunlight and under certain weather conditions, this process starts a chain reaction. The reaction breaks down ever-increasing numbers of ozone molecules. As many as 100,000 molecules of ozone can be destroyed by a single free atom of chlorine, before the chlorine atom bonds with other atoms to form a stable molecule. These CFCs are destroying the stratosphere's ozone far quicker than new stratospheric ozone is being created. Since, ground-level ozone breaks down without rising into the stratosphere, the ozone layer is not replenished from below.

Scientists are concerned about the thinning of the ozone layer because of the risk that increased UV exposure poses for humans and other animals. You have probably heard of the "ozone hole" that forms over Antarctica every year. While it is not really a hole, just an area of reduced ozone, it is responsible for increased UV radiation at the South Pole and over portions of Australia. Increased UV radiation may lead to skin cancer. It also may contribute to the disappearance of amphibians around the world, as their eggs are destroyed by UV.

In 1987, most nations of the world signed the Montreal Protocol (followed by other treaties). The agreement called for the nations of the world to ban the use of CFCs and other ozone-destroying chemicals.

The Mesosphere and Thermosphere

Above the stratosphere is the mesosphere, which extends from about 55 to 90 km above Earth. Here, the temperature once again decreases with altitude to about -86°C. As in the troposphere, vertical movement of air occurs in the mesosphere. During the summer, enough convection can occur to form thin clouds, visible from the ground near sunset. Beyond the mesosphere lies the thermosphere, which is bombarded by intense solar radiation. Thermosphere temperature increases very rapidly due to absorption of solar radiation by the sparsely scattered molecules. The top of this layer can reach temperatures as high as 1500°C, depending on the level of solar activity.

Analysis Questions

1. In what layer of the atmosphere do you live?

2. What is ozone and where in the atmosphere does it occur?

3. What has been destroying the ozone layer and why is its destruction a serious problem?

4. In which layer of the atmosphere does weather take place?

5. Answer the essential question: *What are the major differences between the troposphere, stratosphere, and mesosphere?*

Plumes and Dispersion

Essential Question: How do atmospheric conditions affect the dispersal of smokestack pollutants?

Overview

Read the following article. Answer the analysis questions.

Smokestacks and Plumes

When emissions are released into the air from a smokestack, they are carried away by the air. The air in the atmosphere is constantly moving in currents that are similar to the currents in bodies of water. We call the currents in the atmosphere winds. The winds that carry pollution from smokestacks are mostly confined to the troposphere, the lowest layer of the atmosphere.

The primary cause of wind currents in the troposphere is differences in temperature between areas on the surface of the Earth. When an area on the surface of the Earth heats up, the surface heat is conducted to the air above it, causing the air to heat up as well. When air in the atmosphere heats up, it spreads out and becomes less dense, which causes it to rise above surrounding, denser air, just the way a helium balloon rises through denser air. When one area of the Earth's surface is warmer than another, the less dense air over the warm area will rise and the denser air from the cooler area is drawn horizontally along the Earth's surface to fill in where the warmer air is rising. (Areas where the air is rising are called low pressure zones and areas of sinking air are called high pressure zones.) These temperature differences cause horizontal winds along the Earth's surface.

Scientists use their understanding of air movement in the troposphere to predict how pollutants will travel based on conditions of air pressure, temperature, wind, and other factors. They also look at the emission rate, smokestack height and diameter, exit speed, and the temperature of the pollution.

Scientists call the path that pollution takes through the atmosphere a *plume*. Imagine putting a drop of food coloring into a bathtub as it is filling with water. The drop will gradually spread out through the tub, being carried by the currents caused by the incoming flow of water. The shape of the colored water is a plume.

Knowing the size and shape of the plume from a smokestack can enable scientists to understand how pollutants from the smokestack are getting distributed. When power companies build a new power plant, they can predict where the emissions from the power plant will travel by looking at the weather patterns in the area.

One way power plants reduce the impact of their emissions is by building taller smokestacks. Building a taller smokestack allows the emissions to spread over a larger area. Just as your sand was spread over a larger area when you blew it from a higher height, the emissions from a taller smokestack have the opportunity to spread over a larger area before descending to the surface. The idea behind spreading pollution over a larger area is to decrease the amount of pollution affecting any specific area. The effect of many pollutants depends on their concentration. The concentration of a substance is the amount of that substance found in a particular area or volume. So, taller smokestacks mean the plume can spread over a larger area, and the concentration of the pollutants in any particular area will be lower.

Analysis Questions

1. List three aspects of the atmosphere that affect how pollution moves through the air.

2. What causes winds on the Earth?

3. Suppose pollution with a temperature of 20°C is released from a smokestack into air that is 18°C. Will the pollution rise up into the air or fall to the ground? Why?

4. Answer the essential question: *How do atmospheric conditions affect the dispersal of smokestack pollutants?*

Air Movement in Wisconsin

? **Essential Question:** *What other states will feel the effects of emissions from a coal-burning power plant built in southern Wisconsin?*

Overview

As you have already learned, power plants emit nitrogen oxides (NO_x) and sulfur dioxide (SO_2) into the atmosphere. Both compounds contribute to acid deposition. Both compounds break down and begin to form acids within a few days. In this activity, you will predict where the wind will carry sulfur dioxide and nitrogen oxide emissions from a power plant built in southern Wisconsin.

Materials

colored pencils
ruler

Analysis Questions

1. Look at the map showing wind direction in the eastern region of the United States. Locate the southern region of Wisconsin (the state that is circled). Record the wind direction in southern Wisconsin.

2. Of the environmental impacts of coal-burning power plants that you have learned about in this chapter, which is most affected by the wind?

3. Pollution that travels through the atmosphere can remain in the air for several days before rain or gravity pulls it toward Earth. How far can pollution travel while it remains in the air? *Calculate how far pollution from a power plant in southern Wisconsin will travel if a typical wind speed for southern Wisconsin is 8 miles per hour.*

   a. Distance in one day:
   b. Distance in two days:
   c. Distance in three days:

4. On the map of the U.S. on the next page, draw the plume of SO_2 and NO_x that would develop as it leaves the southern Wisconsin power plant. Use your previous answers to determine how far the pollution would travel. Use the arrows to determine the direction in which it would travel.

5. Answer the essential question: *Which states will feel the effects of emissions from a coal-burning power plant built in southern Wisconsin?*

Wind Speed in Wisconsin

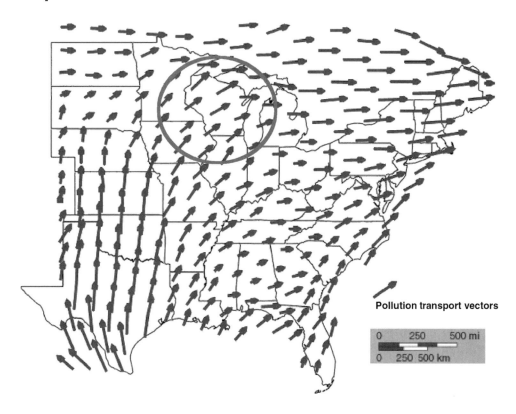

Pollution transport vectors

Figure 1: Typical wind patterns in the eastern U.S. Source: The Natural Resources Defense Council

Why do We Burn Coal for Electricity?

Essential Question: *Given the environmental impacts of coal combustion, does it make sense to continue to burn coal to generate electricity?*

Overview

In this chapter, you have learned about several harmful impacts of burning coal to generate electricity. You have also learned about ways to decrease these harmful impacts through pollution-reduction technologies. You know from previous chapters that increasing the efficiency of electricity generation or reducing the demand for energy can also reduce harmful impacts. However, pollution-reduction technologies, increasing efficiency, and decreasing demand cannot eliminate the harmful effects of coal power plants entirely. Therefore, we should consider the question of why we still burn coal to generate electricity in the United States.

The first thing we need to recognize is that every process for generating electricity has costs. Some of those costs are financial, and some of them are environmental, like the effects of pollution from coal power plants. Some costs must be paid immediately, and others can be spread over long periods of time. Some only affect the people who use the electricity or the power plant's local environment, and others affect a much larger community and geographic region. When our society makes decisions about what sources of energy we use, we have to weigh those costs in light of our values. The Environmental Decision-Making process you use in this course is designed to help you weigh costs in this way.

In Chapter 6, you will investigate the benefits, environmental impacts, and financial costs of energy sources other than fossil fuels. To do so, you will learn about ways to generate electricity other than burning materials to make steam to turn a turbine. Some of these alternatives produce no harmful emissions.

Even oil and natural gas, the other two plentiful forms of fossil fuel, produce less harmful emissions than coal. The combustion of oil and natural gas produces harmful emissions, but in lower quantities than oil. Oil combustion releases approximately the same amount of SO_2, and two-thirds the NO_x of coal combustion. Natural gas combustion produces less than one-third the NO_x and less than 1% the SO_2 of coal combustion. Despite the lower emissions of oil and natural gas, coal is the dominant source of electricity in the U.S. In 2004, coal was the source of approximately 45% of the electric power generated in the U.S., natural gas was the source of approximately 14%, and oil was the source of less than 3%.

Reasons for continuing to burn coal

If there are alternatives to coal that produce less harmful emissions, why does the U.S. continue to burn coal to generate electricity?

The first reason that the U.S. burns coal to generate electricity is financial. In the U.S. coal is plentiful and relatively inexpensive to mine and transport. That makes coal an inexpensive source of energy for the United States. Even with the added costs of reducing the environmental impacts of mining and combustion, burning coal is cheaper or comparable to other sources of energy. While the costs of some alternatives to coal, including oil and natural gas, are comparable to coal, their supplies are limited. So, switching to another source of energy would either cause shortages of those alternative energy sources for other uses or drive up their prices. For example, if large numbers of coal burning power plants were converted to oil, they would compete with cars, trucks, trains, and airplanes for the oil that their fuel is made from. So, one way to keep oil and natural gas available and affordable for powering vehicles and heating homes and businesses is to continue burning coal for electricity.

The second reason is historical. Coal has been used as a source of energy in the U.S. for a very long time. Even before the first electrical power plants, coal was burned to heat buildings and to turn steam turbines that were used to drive machinery in factories and railroad locomotives. Throughout the 1900s, large numbers of coal-burning power plants were constructed. People have known for a long time that the smoke from burning coal looked dirty and could cause people to cough. However, scientists have only recently learned about many of the impacts of coal emissions. It was only in the 1970s and 80s that scientists connected the loss of trees in certain forests to acid rain and traced the acid back to distant power plants and factories. And more recently, scientists found a connection between particulate emissions and the occurrence of asthma in downwind communities. It was only in the last decade that scientists became aware that mercury levels in deep-sea fish were rising and that coal combustion was contributing to the increase in mercury levels in the oceans.

Many of the coal-burning power plants built in the last century are no longer in use or have been converted to burn other fuels. However, many coal-burning power plants are still in use. The cost of replacing a coal-burning power plant with another form of power plant is very high. For that reason, many power companies have chosen to upgrade existing coal-burning power plants to be more efficient and have lower emissions, rather than replace them with other sources of energy.

The third reason to continue burning coal for electricity is political. The U.S. has been concerned for a long time about depending too much on other countries to supply its energy needs. Having a sufficient supply of energy at an affordable price is important for maintaining America's economy and quality of life. The U.S. has a much larger supply of coal than it does of other sources of fossil fuel. For example, the U.S. imports most of the oil that it uses from other countries. In recent history, the supply of oil to the U.S. and its prices have been affected by events in other countries, including natural disasters, war, and political unrest. If the U.S. can limit its dependence on oil, it will be less affected by events in other countries. For that reason, policymakers have decided to continue to rely on coal to generate electricity.

Clean Coal Technology and the future of coal power plants

The United States is not the only country that views coal as an energy source for the 21st century. England, Australia, and China are all pursuing strategies for electricity generation that include coal as an important component. However, the governments and energy companies in those countries are also concerned about the harmful impacts of burning coal on humans and the natural environment. So scientists and engineers those countries are developing and installing technologies that can increase the efficiency of coal plants and reduce their harmful emissions.

These technologies include:

- Combined cycle technologies that achieve dramatically higher efficiency than conventional coal power plants. This approach first uses the flow of the exhaust gases produced by combustion to power one turbine. Next the heat of those gases is used to boil water and produce steam that powers a second turbine.

- Scrubbers that remove SO_2 from emissions by passing them through lime or another alkaline substance that absorbs the sulfur.

- Control systems that maintain lower temperatures in the burners, reducing the formation of NO_x during the combustion of the coal.

- Scrubbers that remove NO_x from emissions by causing the NO_x in the exhaust gases to react with ammonia, which converts it to water and nitrogen gas (N_2).

- Scrubbers that remove mercury from exhaust gases by passing them through carbon, including partially combusted coal, which absorb the mercury.

- Coal gasification technologies that convert coal and steam into a gaseous mixture by combining them at high temperature and pressure. The resulting gas is passed through filtering systems that remove up to 99% of the sulfur and other impurities and then burned. Because the impurities are removed before combustion, the level of harmful emissions is extremely low.

Some of these technologies are already in widespread use, such as SO_2 scrubbers, and others are still under investigation, such as mercury scrubbers. In combination, they have the potential to dramatically reduce harmful emissions while increasing efficiency.

Analysis Questions

1. What are the environmental costs of burning coal to generate electricity?

2. What are the financial costs of burning coal to generate electricity? In other words, what are the major costs that the power company has to pay over the lifetime of a coal-burning power plant?

3. How do the emissions that result from burning coal for electricity compare to the impacts of burning oil and natural gas?

4. What are the major reasons why the U.S. burns coal for electricity today?

5. At what stages in the power plant process can actions be taken to reduce harmful emissions?

6. Answer the essential question: *Given the environmental impacts of coal combustion, does it make sense to continue to burn coal to generate electricity?*

Plant Siting

Chapter 4
Plant Siting

Connections

The last two chapters gave you a background on how fossil fuel burning power plants work. They also described the major environmental impacts of using fossil fuels to generate electricity. This chapter provides a chance to apply that information to a real-life situation. The problem is faced by a community in southeastern Wisconsin that needs a new power plant. Communities across the country make decisions like this regularly. In making such decisions, citizens balance the need for power with the power plant's negative impacts on the environment.

In the case study in this chapter, you must build a coal-burning power plant. In a later chapter, you will have the option to use alternative forms of electricity generation. The skills you learn in this chapter involve choosing a site for a coal-burning power plant. You will also use them later as you face a more complex decision.

In this chapter:

In this chapter, you will use the Environmental Decision Making process. You will develop a solution to the common problem of choosing a location for a power plant. During the process, you will investigate southeastern Wisconsin, as you look for the best place to locate a coal-burning power plant in that region. You will keep track of stakeholders and consequences. Finally, you will make a decision that is supported by evidence. Much of this evidence will come from your analysis of data about the region. This data will include the area's resources, its population patterns, and the land available for use. You will be using *ArcView* as your analysis tool.

When you're done you'll be able to:

*   Assess available resources in an area to determine if it is an appropriate site for a power plant.

*   Identify all stakeholders in a decision, including environmental stakeholders who may not have the ability to speak for themselves.

*   Use scientific evidence to defend decisions based on sound judgment.

Lesson 1
Midwest Power

 Driving Question: *What are we trying to accomplish while choosing the location for a power plant?*

Overview

In this lesson, you'll review the power problem introduced in the first chapter of this unit. First, you will read a description of the problem and why it is difficult to solve. Southeast Wisconsin needs a new power plant, and the community has chosen coal as fuel for that plant. You should refer back to what you learned in the **Impacts** chapter to determine the consequences of building this type of power plant. Finally, you and your team will work together to reach consensus about how to solve the problem.

Important Content

- When determining the best way to generate electricity for a community, it is important to look at the available local resources.

- There are many issues surrounding power generation, including cost, land use changes, efficiency considerations, the sustainability for different environments, byproducts generated, and their environmental impacts.

Midwest Power, Inc.

 Essential Question: What factors will you need to consider as you make your decision?

Overview

Your task force is assigned to evaluate the electricity problem in southeastern Wisconsin. You will work with a local power company, Midwest Power, to solve the problem. The power company has chosen the best size for the power plant, based on population projections and operating costs. They have also selected a general area where the power should be generated to ensure that all citizens in the growing region have access to electricity. Your contribution to the team will be in your understanding of coal power plants, the resources they need, and the impacts they have on the environment.

Procedure

Read the letter on the next page from Midwest Power to your task force. It outlines the basic needs of the power plant that will be built. It also gives details for the report that you will provide to the company.

To begin the process, write answers to the following questions.

Analysis Questions

1. What are the inputs of a coal-burning power plant? Where will you find these resources?

2. What is an appropriate location for a coal-burning power plant? Why?

3. What concerns will residents living near a coal-burning power plant have?

4. Answer the essential question: *What factors will you need to consider as you make your decision?*

Midwest Power, Inc. Letter

Dear Environmental Scientist task force:

The Board of Directors of Midwest Power, Inc. has completed its review of power supply and demand in your region. At last week's meeting, the Board decided to increase our operations in the southern Wisconsin market. We intend to proceed with initial locating plans for a coal-burning power plant to be built in the Lake Geneva, Wisconsin area. This region has a temperate climate with rolling farmland, many lakes and streams. It also has many hard-working and honest people who may soon join the Midwest Power family.

I would like your task force to prepare a location report for Midwest Power, Inc. The report should describe the best location within this area to locate a coal-burning power plant. The chosen location should facilitate the movement of resources to and from the power plant. It should also be welcomed by the local population. It also needs to be both economically and environmentally sound.

Our engineers have decided that a 350-megawatt plant is needed to meet the electricity needs of the region. Our engineers require the plant to be located on the shores of a lake with at least 13,000,000 cubic meters of water for cooling purposes. The plant needs to be close to railroads because rail is by far the most economical method for shipping coal. Highway access is also important. The plant must be located on land that is both affordable and that minimizes any potential for negative environmental impact.

Please prepare a report that contains a list of the top three locations in the area for this coal-burning plant. Include a rationale for each of the sites on your list and an explanation of the techniques you used to reach your decision. I will review the list and forward it to the Board of Directors for the final decision.

I appreciate your willingness to tackle this challenging and important task.

Sincerely,

Keisha Hendricks

Keisha Hendricks,
CEO

Lake Geneva, Wisconsin

? *Essential Question:* What is life like in Lake Geneva, Wisconsin?

Overview

To come up with a good plan for siting the power plant, you need to learn what life is like in southeastern Wisconsin. Read the following description of Lake Geneva, a typical town in the area. Then answer the questions below.

Map

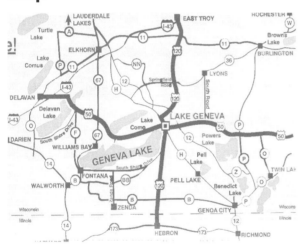

Description of Lake Geneva

The Lake Geneva Region

Lake Geneva is located in southeastern Wisconsin, about 10 miles north of the Illinois state line. It is 75 miles north of Chicago and 45 miles southeast of Milwaukee. Residents sometimes travel to these large cities to shop or for recreation.

Lake Geneva offers the benefits and beauties of a four-season way of life. The region gets on average 48 inches of snow each winter. Summer temperatures are generally moderate; averaging 78 to 80 degrees F. Heat waves do hit the region in summer, however. In the fall, city dwellers may travel to the Lake Geneva area to enjoy the colors of its fall foliage.

The population of Lake Geneva has been rising steadily, but it still retains its small-town flavor. In 1999, the Lake Geneva population was about 6,700, up from 6,175 in 1994. The majority of residents in Lake Geneva and nearby Burlington are working and middle class. Burlington's population is becoming more ethnically diverse, as Mexican immigrants move to the area. Lake Geneva, with its gorgeous waterfront and luxury homes, resorts, and golf clubs attracts more wealthy residents. Tourism is also an important industry in Lake Geneva. People visit the area for its natural beauty and its outdoor recreation. These are local characteristics residents prize and want to preserve.

Tourism is important in Burlington, too. Burlington was once part of the Underground Railroad, which helped escaped slaves fleeing the South find safety in the North. People around the region also visit to celebrate the annual Chocolate Festival in mid-May.

Most people in the region–both residents and visitors–enjoy outdoor activities. In Lake Geneva, water sports and fishing are popular. The entire region has a lovely landscape, with rolling green hills, lakes, and ponds. Hiking and camping are popular. In winter, the area is a magnet for skiers.

Residents and visitors appreciate Lake Geneva's old-time, small-town atmosphere. The pace of life is slower than in the hectic cities. Residents are generally conservative and church-going, but also welcome newcomers. As this small town grows, its power needs are increasing. Most residents of the Lake Geneva/Burlington area have never had to make such important decisions involving growth and energy. Their quiet, rural lifestyle has attracted more people to the area. Now they must confront the energy issues associated with their growth.

Analysis Questions

1. Based on this reading, what values do the residents of this area feel are most important? How would these values affect the siting of the power plant?

2. Answer the essential question using the information from the map and brochure. *What is life like in Lake Geneva, Wisconsin?*

3. What additional information will you need to know about the region before you make your decision for Midwest Power, Inc.?

The City of Lake Geneva, WI • Community Profile

Location & Climate

Lake Geneva is located in southeastern Wisconsin, 10 miles north of the Illinois state line, 75 miles north of Chicago and 45 miles southeast of Milwaukee. Interstate 43 is six miles to the north and Interstate 94 is 27 miles to the east.

Climate

Lake Geneva offers a four-season way of life—white winters, green spring & summers, & colorful falls.

Average Temperatures (°F)	High	Low
Spring	53	35
Summer	78	59
Fall	59	42
Winter	30	16

Annual precipitation: 35"
Annual snowfall: 48"

Population

Year	City Population
1994	6,175
1995	6,389
1996	6,426
1997	6,453
1998	6,548
1999	6,700

Education

Public Schools

	Enrollment
Badger High School	1,012
Lake Geneva Middle School	580
Dennison Middle School	389
Central Elementary School	264
Eastview Elementary School	253
Star Central Elementary	138
District Office	

Parochial

Faith Christian School	235
First Evangelical Lutheran	65
Mt. Zion Christian Temple	88
St. Francis De Sales	240

Higher Education

Gateway Technical	2,391
UW-Whitewater	9,780

Airports

General Mitchell International Airport

Grand Geneva Resort & Spa

O'Hare International Chicago

Southeastern Wisconsin: Area Profile

Counties involved in power plant decision:

County	1990 Population	2000 Population	% increase
Rock	139,731	152,307	9%
Walworth	75,007	93,759	25%
Kenosha	127,843	149,577	17%
Racine	174,844	188,831	8%
Waukesha	305,735	360,767	18%
Jefferson	67,909	74,021	9%
TOTAL	**891,069**	**1,019,262**	**14%**

Projected population in 2010: 1,200,000

Constraints

Essential Question: *What are your constraints and considerations in selecting a location for a power plant?*

Overview

Think about decisions in terms of constraints and considerations. They can help you make sense of a complicated problem where many factors affect your final choice. Constraints describe the limitations you must work with. They may be either physical limitations or limitations that come from your personal values. For example, if there are only certain resources available to you, that would be a physical constraint. If you are unwilling to destroy the habitat of an endangered species, that would be a values-based constraint. Constraints include time, money, laws, or the environmental impacts you are unwilling to tolerate.

Constraints are absolute limitations. They cannot be violated in a solution. Considerations are preferences that might or might not be possible. Decision makers work to achieve the most important considerations the best they can. They also keep in mind their constraints as they consider all of the available options.

Procedure

Determine your personal constraints and considerations regarding the siting of the coal-burning power plant in Lake Geneva, WI.

Analysis Questions

1. What is your ultimate goal for this decision?

2. In an ideal world, what would you consider a successful outcome?

3. Which of your personal values will affect your considerations list?

4. Answer the essential question: *What are your constraints and considerations for selecting a location for a power plant?*

Group Constraints and Considerations

Essential Question: What made some considerations more important than others?

Overview

When environmental decisions need to be made, there are often groups of people with very different ideas about the problem. So far, the decisions you have made have been personal ones. In this project, you will work with your group to make a decision that you can all agree on. You must reach a consensus. You each have your own lists of constraints and considerations. Some parts of your lists will be the same and some will be different. Your task today is to agree on a list that will guide your group through the rest of the project. It is important to agree on your goals now, before you continue with the Environmental Decision Making Process in later lessons.

Materials

lists of personal constraints and considerations from each group member letter from Lesson 1: *Midwest Power, Inc.*

Procedure

As a group, you must reach an agreement about the constraints and considerations you will use to make your decision. Remember that constraints are goals that you must reach or rules that you must not violate. Considerations are goals that you would like to achieve but are not absolutely necessary.

Analysis Questions

1. What are the absolute constraints that your group agrees should not be violated in this scenario?

2. What are the considerations that you would like to achieve in this scenario?

3. Rank your considerations from most to least important.

4. Answer the essential question: *What made some considerations more important than others?* Write at least a two-paragraph justification of your ranking.

Lesson 2

Exploring Lake Geneva

Driving Question: *What are the environmental impacts of building a power plant on this land?*

Overview

In this lesson, you will use your group's list of constraints and criteria as a guide and narrow down your options to the three best ones. As in the last lesson, you will work by yourself and with your group. Your task will be to find the best locations for the coal-burning power plant in the Lake Geneva, Wisconsin region. To explore the consequences of these sitings, you will use Cascading Consequence Charts. Once the consequences are clear, you will move on to the next lesson to define your stakeholders.

Important Content

• Because of water withdrawals from lakes, and temperature differences in water returned to lakes, power plants can have serious impacts on lakes where they are located.

• Each part of the power plant: the boiler, stack, turbine, cooling tower, and water system involves different energy transformations.

Lakes

Essential Question: *Based on nearby lakes, what are the best locations for a coal power plant?*

Overview

In this activity, you will use *ArcView* to look at a map of the area surrounding Lake Geneva, Wisconsin. This map describes the area that Midwest Power, Inc. has proposed as a location for a new coal-burning power plant. You are going to determine which lakes have an adequate volume of water for the power plant. Your goal is to choose the best location for the power plant based on lake volume. In the next several activities, you'll investigate the other factors that will influence your power plant location decision.

Materials

ArcView 3.2 installed on a Windows computer

Lake Geneva Coal Plant Project ArcView file
File name: GenevaCoalProject.apr

Procedure

1. Open the Lake Geneva Coal Project ArcView file according to your teacher's instructions.

2. Look at the Lake Michigan Regional Map. (Select it from the Geneva Coal Project menu if it is not visible at startup.) Notice that the window displays the states of Wisconsin (orange), Illinois (red), Michigan (beige), and Indiana (yellow). Locate the purple rectangle called Lake Geneva Map Area. This purple rectangle represents the area where Midwest Power, Inc. wants to locate a coal power plant. Minimize Lake Michigan. Close the Regional Map view and open the Local Map view.

3. Use the Find tool to locate the body of water, "Lake Geneva." Record the name of the lake on the data table, as well as the latitude (north and south) and longitude (east and west) of the center of the lake.

4. Using the Identify tool , record the surface area in square meters (m²), average depth in meters (m), and volume of Lake Geneva on your data table.

5. Besides Lake Geneva, what other lakes are large enough to supply a power plant? Using the Query tool , find all the lakes that fit the minimum volume requirement of 13,000,000 m³.

6. Record the name, longitude, latitude, surface area, average depth, and volume of these lakes on your data table.

ArcView Tip

When using the Query tool [icon], double click a Field from the left, choose a quantifier, and choose a Value by double clicking on the appropriate name. Press New Set to display the selected. To view what was selected, open the theme table [icon] with the Bodies Of Water theme active. To view the selected body of water's features, use the "Promote" button [icon] to move the selected (highlighted in yellow) features to the top of the table. This makes it easier to view all the data for all the features.

Be sure to enter values in the query without using scientific notation or units.

Analysis Questions

1. What are the two largest lakes in the region?

2. What are the two deepest lakes?

3. Do you think there is any reason that a deep lake would be better than a shallow lake for a power plant? Why?

4. Think back to what you learned about environmental effects on the aquatic food web. Describe what you think the lake will look like in 5 years? In 10 years?

5. Answer the essential question: *Based on nearby lakes, what are the best locations for a coal power plant?*

Lakes Data Table

#	Lake Name	Latitude (°)	Longitude (°)	Area (m²)	Average Depth (m)	Volume (m³)
1						
2						
3						
4						
5						
6						
7						
8						
9						

Land Use

Essential Question: Based on land use in this area, what are the best three locations for a coal-burning power plant?

Overview

Now that you have found lakes large enough to support a 350-megawatt power plant, where will you place the plant? Will you purchase land in a residential area? In a forest? In this lesson, you will explore the *land use* surrounding each lake. You will think about the implications of building a power plant in areas with different types of land use. A power plant requires 20,234 m² (5 acres) of land just for the buildings and storage for the plant. Keep this in mind as you look at different sites, so you can be sure the area is large enough for the power plant.

You have learned that power plants emit dangerous gases that pollute the environment. You have also learned about other environmental effects that power plants cause. These effects are usually seen locally, but they can spread long distances. All of the possible power plant locations you are researching are in the same area of Wisconsin. So, their long-distance effects will be very similar. However, areas nearer the power plant could see very different and more serious effects.

The buffer is an important tool for environmental scientists who use geographic information systems. A buffer extends the area of an object on a map, making it easy to visualize the vicinity surrounding the selection. In this activity, you will use *ArcView* to create buffers around each of the nine lakes you identified in the previous activity.

Materials

 ArcView 3.2 installed on a Windows compute

 Lake Geneva Coal Plant Project ArcView file
File name: GenevaCoalProject.apr

Procedure Part 1: Advantages and Disadvantages

1. There are six different Land Use types that are shown in the *ArcView* theme.

- Agriculture and livestock
- Commerce, Industry, and Service
- Forests and Wetlands
- Lakes and Reservoirs
- Residence and Mixed-Use Urban
- Unknown Use

For each land-use type, write down one advantage and one disadvantage in locating a coal-burning power plant within this area. Be prepared to share your results with the class.

Procedure Part 2: Identifying Land Use using *ArcView*

1. Open the Lake Geneva Map Area view within the Lake Geneva Coal Power Plant project. Select and activate the Land Use theme. Use the Find tool [image] to locate Lake Geneva.

2. Record the land-use type at the lakeshore of Lake Geneva on your data table.

3. Assume that a circle within a radius of 5 km around the lake will feel most of the effects of your power plant. Create a buffer of 5 km around this lake. (See below for specific instructions about creating a buffer.)

4. In your notebook, describe the land-use area within the 5 km buffer. List what you think most of the people who live in the circle would use the land for.

5. Describe any potential environmental effects that could come from locating a power plant in this location. Record your ideas on your data table.

6. Repeat the above procedure for the remaining lakes you identified in the last activity. To save time, you can construct the same query you made in the last activity. Then create buffers for all the selected lakes at once.

Analysis Questions

1. Which land-use type do you think is the most appropriate for a power plant? Why?

2. How many of the lakes described on your data table have this as their most common land use in their proximity?

3. What complications might arise from building on a lake that has many different types of land use?

4. Which of the lakeshore locations would affect a large residential area?

5. Would any of the lakeshore sites affect forested areas? What environmental impacts will a coal-burning power plant have on forests and vegetation?

6. Answer the essential question: *Based on land use in this area, what are the best three locations for a coal-burning power plant?*

Using *ArcView* to Create a Buffer

A buffer is a zone of specific distance around a feature. Follow these steps to create a buffer in *ArcView*.

1. Select the object you'd like to make a buffer around and select **Create Buffers** from the **Theme** menu. You'll see the first screen in the Buffer Wizard, as shown in Figure 1.

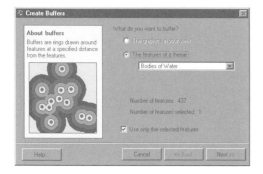

Figure 1: Buffer Wizard, Step 1. Be sure that "Use only the selected features" is selected.

2. On Screen 1 (see Figure 1), select what you want to buffer. Click the check box for "Use only selected features," then click Next. You'll see the second screen.

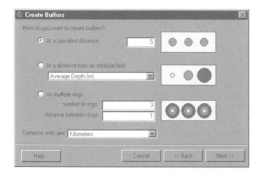

Figure 2: Buffer Wizard, Step 2. This screen tells ArcView what kind of buffer to make.

3. On Screen 2 (Figure 2), select the distance you'd like the buffer to reach. Be sure that the units you select are kilometers and click Next. You will see the third screen.

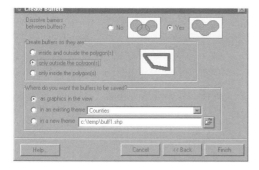

Figure 3: Buffer Wizard, Step 3. This screen sets formatting options for the buffer.

4. On Screen 3 (Figure 3), set the formatting options for the buffer. When creating buffers for lakes, select buffers that are only outside the polygon(s). Save the buffers as graphics in the current view.

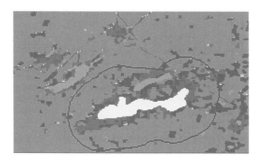

Figure 4: A 5 km buffer around Lake Geneva, WI.

5. An example of a 5 km buffer around a lake is shown in Figure 4. The buffer can be removed by selecting it with the arrow and deleting.

Land Use

#	Lake Name	Land Use (at lakeshore)	Land Use (within 5 km circle)	Potential Environmental Effects
1				
2				
3				
4				
5				
6				
7				
8				
9				

Roads and Railroads

Essential Question: *Based on proximity to roads and railroads, what are the three best locations for a coal power plant?*

Overview

Midwest Power, Inc's new power plant will be constructed in southeastern Wisconsin. You have learned that much of the good-quality coal is located many miles away, in states like Wyoming and Tennessee. How will the coal get to your power plant? The coal will have to be transported in large trucks on the road or in train cars. The cost associated with transporting coal should be part of your decision of where to build a power plant. A location without nearby roads would cost the power company extra expenses. They would have to build an access road or rail spur to deliver many tons of coal to the power plant each day.

Materials

  ArcView 3.2 installed on a Windows computer

  Lake Geneva Coal Plant Project ArcView file
File name: GenevaCoalProject.apr

Procedure

1. Open the Lake Geneva Map Area view within the Lake Geneva Coal Plant project. Turn on the Railroads and Land Use themes.

2. Make the Bodies of Water theme active by clicking on it. Use the Find tool [image] to locate the first lake on your data tables from previous activities. The lake should turn from blue to yellow, indicating the lake was found and selected by *ArcView*.

3. Use the Zoom-in tool [image] to draw a rectangle around the lake, so it includes the lake and a nearby railroad.

4. Observe the land use around the lake. Choose a specific location where you would like to locate the power plant. (Remember the costs and benefits you listed in Unit 1, Chapter 4, Lesson 1: *Land Use*) Record the lake name on your data table, as well as the latitude (north and south) and longitude (east and west) of the potential power plant location. The area (footprint) of the power plant will be 0.02 km² (5 acres).

5. Use the Measure tool [image] to determine the distance from your chosen location to the nearest railroad. Click first on the proposed power plant location, then click on the nearest railroad. Record this distance on the data table. (For more information, see the section on the Measure tool below.)

6. Identify one potential power plant location at each lake. Record it in your data table and use *ArcView* to measure the amount of railroad distance.

7. Once you have recorded all the distances to railroads, turn off the Railroads theme. Turn on the Roads & Highways theme and repeat the above process for roads.

Analysis Questions

1. Which lakes are close to both railroads and roads?

2. Do you think highway or railroad would be better for transporting thousands of tons of coal each day? Why?

3. Answer the essential question: Be sure to justify your response. *Based on proximity to roads and railroads, what are the three best locations for a coal power plant?*

Using the Measure Tool in *ArcView*

The measure tool is used to measure the distance between points on a map in *ArcView*. It uses the standard units for the theme that is currently selected. For *Investigations*, most results with the measure tool will be in kilometers (km).

1. Select the measure tool. Click once on the starting location (the lakeshore). Notice that as you move the mouse, you are dragging a line from the click-point to the mouse location. Notice that the length of that line is displayed in the lower left corner of the window.

2. Then click on the next location (the power plant site). Lastly, click on the shore of the lake. You should have a line that connects the power plant to both a railroad line and the lake.

3. In the lower left corner of the *ArcView* window are two numbers: segment length and a total length. Record the length in your data table. (Segment length is the distance between two of the points on your line, perhaps between the power plant and the lake. The "length" shows the total distance from rail to power plant to lake.)

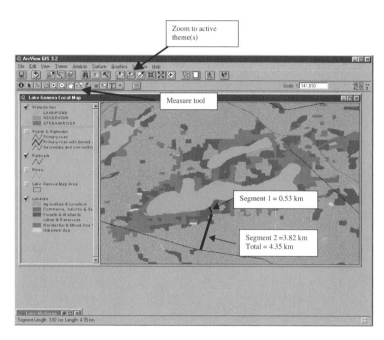

Figure 2: The Measure Tool in *ArcView*

Roads and Railroads

	Site	Latitude (degrees)	Longitude (degrees)	Road Distance (km)	Railroad Distance (km)
1					
2					
3					
4					
5					
6					
7					
8					
9					

Narrowing Options

Essential Question: *How do the three choices fit the constraints and considerations YOU feel are most important?*

Overview

In this activity, you will explore the three best options you chose in the last activity. As you discuss the different options, remember to use evidence to support your point of view. Use the readings from the **Impacts** chapter to better understand the consequences of altering the environment. Use your group's list of constraints and considerations to guide your choices and eliminate unsuitable options.

Procedure

In your group, discuss the options that were developed. Select the best three possibilities. Draw consequence charts to help you make your decision. Make sure that the options you choose meet your constraints and considerations.

Analysis Questions

1. For each of the three options, your group should develop:

   a. a sketch or complete description of the location and the lake where it will get its water;

   b. a Cascading Consequence Chart describing consequences to the environment, the community and the lake ecosystem. The charts should answer these questions.

      i. What types of land are being covered by the power plant? What effect will that have on the food web?

      ii. What other kinds of land/cities will be affected by the emissions and waste products of the power plant?

      iii. What effects will the placement of buildings have on the residents who live around the lake?

2. Answer the essential question: *How do the three choices fit the constraints and considerations YOU feel are most important?*

Lesson 3
Decision

Driving Question: *Which of the options has the smallest number of unintended consequences?*

Overview

Using the consequence charts from the last lesson, you will continue to explore the consequences of your chosen site for the power plant. With your team, you will identify your stakeholders and determine how important they are to your decision. To organize this information, you will use the Stakeholders Chart from the environmental decision making process. This chart will help you see how different stakeholders will be affected by your actions. By the end of the lesson, you will make your final decision and present it to your classmates. Use all of the information you have gathered in this chapter and unit to explain your decision.

Important Content

- There are many issues surrounding power generation, including cost, land-use changes, efficiency considerations, impacts and sustainability for different environments, and byproducts generated.

- The area affected by a power plant is larger than the power plant itself. In fact, a power plant can have environmental impacts over hundred to thousands of miles.

Investigate Impacts

Essential Questions: *Which stakeholders will be most affected by your decision? Are those stakeholders the ones who have the power to make the decision?*

Overview

It is time to look at the consequence charts for your three options more closely. In today's activity, you will create stakeholder charts for the options you chose in the last lesson. Remember: stakeholders are people, organizations, the environment, etc., that will be affected by your decision. The charts you create in this activity will help you organize the consequences in a different way. They will give you a picture of all the ways each stakeholder will be affected. It is important to note whether these effects are part of your intended goal, or side effects. Choices that have many unintended side effects might not be the best ones to make. Another aspect of side effects, and negative effects in general, is consent. Did the stakeholder consent to be a part of this process or decision? Think about the responsibilities decision makers have for the consequences of their actions.

Procedure

1. Based on your consequence charts and food webs, create a list of stakeholders.

2. As a group, complete the stakeholders chart for each of the options.

Analysis Questions

1. How did you narrow your list of stakeholders?

2. How are the stakeholders related to your list of constraints and considerations?

3. Do you believe that decision makers are responsible for the unintended effects of the decisions that they make? Why or why not?

4. Answer the essential questions: *Which stakeholders will be most affected by your decision? Are those stakeholders the ones who have the power to make the decision?*

Stakeholders for Option #1

Who are the stakeholders that will be affected by this action?	In what way(s) will they be affected?	+ or −	Is this effect the intended goal of the action or is it a side effect?	Has the stakeholder placed themselves in this position voluntarily and with appropriate understanding of the risks involved?	How important to YOU are the interests of this stakeholder? 1=very important 2= somewhat important 3=unimportant	If the effect is negative, do YOU feel it is directly offset by greater good elsewhere?

Stakeholders for Option #2

Who are the stakeholders that will be affected by this action?	In what way(s) will they be affected?	+ or −	Is this effect the intended goal of the action or is it a side effect?	Has the stakeholder placed themselves in this position voluntarily and with appropriate understanding of the risks involved?	How important to YOU are the interests of this stakeholder? 1=very important 2= somewhat important 3=unimportant	If the effect is negative, do YOU feel it is directly offset by greater good elsewhere?

Stakeholders for Option #3

Who are the stakeholders that will be affected by this action?	In what way(s) will they be affected?	+ or –	Is this effect the intended goal of the action or is it a side effect?	Has the stakeholder placed themselves in this position voluntarily and with appropriate understanding of the risks involved?	How important to YOU are the interests of this stakeholder? 1=very important 2= somewhat important 3=unimportant	If the effect is negative, do YOU feel it is directly offset by greater good elsewhere?

Make a Decision

Essential Question: *What is the best decision? Take into account all stakeholders, consequences, constraints, and considerations.*

Analysis Question

1. Answer the essential question: *What is the best decision? Take into account all stakeholders, consequences, constraints, and considerations.*

Make sure to address each constraint and consideration you listed.

Make sure to explain how any negative effects are outweighed by the positives.

Plant Siting

Present Your Decision

Essential Question: *What were the major obstacles to this decision?*

Overview

An important part of environmental decisions is supporting your claims with evidence. As you prepare your report and presentation, remember that you are trying to convince people that your decision is a good one. Use evidence from the **Fossil Fuels** and **Impacts** chapters to support the decisions you made. Describe logically why you made the decisions. Give reasons why you rejected some options. Include your values and opinions, but make sure what you are saying is also backed up with facts and evidence.

Procedure

Compile a report that includes:

1. a list of your group constraints and considerations

2. a complete description of the three best options

3. consequence charts, and stakeholder charts for all three options

4. a decision statement that describes how you met each constraint and consideration

Answer the analysis questions listed below.

Give a 5-minute presentation that includes:

1. a map of your chosen option

2. a summary of why you chose the option you did

Analysis Questions

1. Are you satisfied with your decision? Why or why not?

2. Is there anything you would change if you had the chance to make the decision again?

3. Answer the essential question: *What were the major obstacles to this decision?*

Global Climate Change

Chapter 5
Global Climate Change

Connections

Most scientists around the world agree that levels of carbon dioxide (CO_2) in the atmosphere are increasing. Today's annual emissions of carbon dioxide are nearly four times as much as they were fifty years ago. There is evidence that this rapid increase in carbon dioxide is contributing to climate change on Earth. This change is often called "global warming" or "global climate change." It is important to understand what effects global climate change could have on our environment. We need more information before we build more power plants and conduct other activities that lead to more CO_2 emissions.

Global climate changes are likely to occur if the current rapid build-up of carbon dioxide in the atmosphere continues. These changes are much more complex than a simple increase in temperature by a few degrees. Weather patterns will change, ocean levels will rise, and deserts will expand. You will be investigating climate change in this chapter. In the next chapter, you will be considering alternative energy sources. One of your considerations will be how much each energy source could contribute to altering Earth's climate.

In this chapter:

In this chapter, you'll learn about scientists' current understanding of global climate change. This topic has been the subject of much debate. Some people claim that there is still uncertainty about how much our climate could change. Others are not certain if it is a result of human combustion of fossil fuels at all. You will learn about the debate and the reasons for the uncertainty.

To understand why human activities may be contributing to global climate change, you must first understand the process that determines climate. You will look at how the Sun heats the Earth. You will look at how geographic features cause differences in climate in different locations. You will also look at how the atmosphere affects climate – the greenhouse effect. You will examine how to identify and measure change in climate. This is difficult because the weather is constantly changing. Finally, you will study our current understanding of normal variations in the Earth's climate system.

When you're done you'll be able to:

- describe the human activities that could contribute to global warming.

- analyze the decisions about energy generation and consumption that could have implications for global climate change.

Lesson 1

The Threat of Global Climate Change

 Driving Question: *Why are some scientists worried about global warming?*

Overview

Global climate change has received a lot of attention in recent years. Scientists have debated whether it is happening, what effects it will have, and what can be done about it. In this lesson, you'll get an overview of current thinking about climate change. You will learn how scientists are gathering more information about it and what might be done. You will explore the claims made about climate change. You will see the evidence that policy makers are using to make decisions about how our actions might affect Earth's climate.

Important Content

- If climate change occurs, the possible effects could include: volatile weather systems, melting ice caps, rising sea levels, and ecosystem changes.

- There has been substantial debate about whether global warming is happening, what is causing it, and what the effects might be. With increasing research, scientists have been able to reduce the uncertainty about these questions.

What is Climate Change?

Essential Question: *Why is there controversy about climate change?*

Overview

The nations of the Earth are currently facing important issues regarding the human impact on the environment. Many scientists have found evidence that emissions of "greenhouse gases" into the atmosphere are leading to a global change in climate. Most predict that if we continue to emit these gases at current rates, we will face changes in temperature, precipitation, and sea level that could threaten life on this planet. Today, you will watch a video that introduces you to different viewpoints about climate change and what may be causing it.

Procedure

Watch the video and answer the questions that follow.

Introduction: Narrator's Point of View

1. There are many different points of views, or opinions, in the debate about global climate change. What appears to be the point of view of this narrator?

Alaska

1. What are the main signs that temperatures have been increasing in Alaska?

2. If global climate change is occurring, which parts of Earth are expected to be the most affected?

3. What are the consequences of increased temperatures in Alaska?

4. What evidence do scientists in the video present to support their argument that Alaska's temperatures are or are not increasing?

5. What are the arguments for and against the idea that humans are causing temperatures to rise?

6. What is the main debate regarding the causes of the current warming trend?

Peru: Qori Kalis Glacier

1. What evidence of climate change is provided by the Qori Kalis glacier? What does this data tell us that the Alaska glaciers do not?

2. Why are glacial ice cores important for learning about past climates?

Nepal & China: Dasudpu Glacier

1. Why is it important to know about past climates?

2. What does the evidence from the glacial ice cores from around the world reveal?

3. What are the different factors scientists suspect might be causing global temperatures to increase?

4. What would we need to know to connect human actions to temperature increases?

East Africa

1. How can climate change lead to increased drought and flooding?

2. Why do scientists and politicians see things differently? Why are politicians more cautious?

3. Answer the essential question: *Why is there controversy about global climate change?*

Predicted Effects

Essential Question: How could climate change affect life on Earth?

Read the following article and answer the analysis questions.

Possible effects of climate change

There is an international committee of scientists called the Intergovernmental Panel on Climate Change (IPCC). Every five years, they release a report on the current scientific understanding of global climate change. In 2001, they issued their third report. Nearly 1000 scientists from around the world were involved in the preparation of that report. The report confirmed that the Earth's climate is changing more rapidly than it has in the past.

According to the 2001 IPCC report, average global temperatures increased by about .6°C (1.0°F) between 1900 and 2000. Currently, temperatures are rising even faster. Scientists predict that temperatures may rise more rapidly in coming decades, perhaps as much as between 1.4°C and 5.8°C (2.5° and 10.4°F). What is the cause of this change in global temperatures? Experts have debated this question over the last 25 years. They are becoming increasingly certain that these changes in temperature are the result of human activities. Scientists believe that the carbon dioxide released when humans burn fossil fuels is primarily responsible for the temperature increases.

In 2001, the IPCC announced that scientific evidence confirms this belief. According to their report, Earth's warming has been caused by an increase in the atmospheric carbon dioxide and other heat-trapping gases released into the atmosphere by human activities. Increased temperatures are just one of the effects of global climate change. Scientists also predict dramatic weather events, rising sea levels, the spread of tropical diseases, and the extinctions of species.

Possible consequence: warmer temperatures

The primary effect of global climate change is an increase in temperature. This is why it is often referred to as global warming. There is evidence that temperatures have already risen dramatically. In fact, scientists believe that the increase in temperatures in the 1900s was the largest in the last 1000 years. It is likely that the 1990s were the warmest decade in that 1000 year period and 1998 was the warmest single year. Even if carbon dioxide emissions are reduced or eliminated, scientists expect this warming trend to speed up over the next 100 years and beyond. They predict that the warming rate will be higher than it has been in the last 10,000 years! The effect of global warming is expected to be greater on land than over the oceans. It has already been shown to be greater at night than during the day. When warming occurs at night, the number of days below freezing is reduced.

An average temperature change of a few degrees doesn't seem very dramatic, but it is. For example, some places will have larger temperature increases than that average. In some places, a warming of a few degrees could mean the difference between a winter with freezing temperatures and a winter with no freezing temperatures. These changes in temperature can cause changes in weather patterns, rising sea-levels, or changes in ecosystems.

Possible consequence: more severe weather events

One change that is predicted with global warming is more severe weather events. Scientists predict that some areas will experience more severe rainstorms and flooding. They predict that there will be more monsoons and hurricanes, and they expect those storms to be more severe. Scientists have observed a 2% to 4% increase in heavy rainstorms in the Northern Hemisphere since 1950.

While some areas will experience more rain, others will experience more severe heat and drought. The effects of heat waves and droughts can be dramatic. For example, in a drought, heat sucks moisture from soil and plants. Thus, there is a greater risk of forest fires. The 1990s saw some of the worst forest fires in U.S. history, as millions of acres burned.

Possible consequence: melting ice and snow

As temperatures rise, snow melts more quickly. Scientists have proven that less ground is being covered in snow during the winter. In many places, the ice cover on lakes and rivers is melting earlier in the year. Glaciers around the world are melting, particularly in mountain valleys. Continental glaciers are melting in Alaska, the Swiss Alps, and especially in tropical regions. By the year 2010, scientists expect the glaciers on top of Mount Kilimanjaro in Africa to be completely melted. The massive ice sheets that cover Greenland are also melting away into the Atlantic.

In the Arctic, the sea ice that once covered the region throughout the winter and much of the summer is disappearing. Arctic sea ice cover declined by 6% between 1978 and 1995. Its thickness has decreased by 40% since the 1960s.

Melting snow and ice has several different effects. As the large amounts of water stored in glaciers runs off into oceans, sea levels rise. Ice and snow also keep temperatures cool by reflecting sunlight. Thus, when snow cover and ice cover are reduced, temperatures increase even more rapidly.

Possible consequence: rising sea levels

Scientists are very concerned about rising sea levels from melting glaciers. As water heats up, it expands, increasing the area it occupies and raising the sea level. Scientists estimate that average sea levels around the world have risen between .1 and .2 meters (3.9 to 7.9 inches) since 1900. The 2001 IPCC report estimated that sea levels could rise as much as .88 meters (34.65 inches or 2.89 feet) by the year 2100. When sea-levels rise, people living close to the coasts are more vulnerable to flooding caused by storms. People who live on islands or at low elevations are particularly at risk. Some of the world's largest cities, like New York, are close to sea-level. In some countries, such as the Netherlands and Bangladesh, much of the land is at or below sea level. In the U.S., more than 50% of the population lives within 50 miles of a coast, a high-risk area for flooding.

Possible consequence: human health

Heat Waves

More frequent and more intense heat waves could result in more heat-related deaths. Heat waves could also increase diseases associated with local air quality problems. These diseases already afflict more than 80 million Americans. In 1999, more than 250 people died as a result of an intense heat wave in the eastern U.S. In 1995, more than 200 people in the city of Chicago died as the result of a heat wave. It is not fair to say that those heat waves were caused by global climate change. However, they are examples of the severe effects that heat waves can have on human health. Scientists do predict increasing numbers of heat waves to accompany global climate change.

Disease

Global climate change can increase the geographic range of diseases. With the increase in temperatures over the last half-century, mosquitoes that carry tropical diseases are now extending their range. Dangerous mosquito-borne illnesses such as dengue fever and malaria are being seen in areas that once were too cold to support the insects. Disease-carrying mosquitoes are also being found at higher elevations where it used to be too cold for the insects. Mosquitoes carrying dengue fever viruses were previously limited to elevations of 3,300 feet but recently appeared at 7,200 feet in the Andes.

Possible consequence: ecosystem shifts and species extinctions

Changes in temperature and other impacts of global climate change are likely to affect ecosystems. This could lead to species extinctions. In North America and Europe, scientists report that birds are migrating, nesting, and rearing young weeks earlier than usual in response to warmer spring temperatures. A recent study found that at least 279 species of plants and animals are already responding to global warming. Species' geographic ranges have shifted toward the poles at an average rate of 4 miles per decade. Over the past 25 years in Antarctica, some penguin populations have shrunk by 33% due to declines in their winter sea-ice habitat. Scientists expect forest tree species to shift northward as the climate warms. Species of plants and animals that cannot adapt to rapid ecosystem changes are likely to become extinct.

Another report indicated that the seasonal changes in water levels in the Great Lakes have altered dramatically in the last 139 years. Scientists have seen the cycle of the annual rising and falling of the Great Lakes now occurs about one month earlier than normal. Scientists say global warming has caused similar "season shifts" around the world. Studies are underway to determine the effects of the altered Great Lakes season shift on aquatic and other wildlife of the region.

Scientists fear that some ecosystems may disappear due to new warmer local climates or coastal sea level rise. These include the alpine meadows in the Rocky Mountains and tropical mangrove forests, In Washington's Olympic Mountains, sub-alpine forest has already invaded higher elevation alpine meadows. In Bermuda, mangrove forests are being lost. In California, shoreline sea life is shifting northward, probably in response to warmer ocean and air temperatures.

Changes in global temperature have occurred in the past, such as during the last ice age, and nature has been able to adapt. However, scientists believe that the current rate of global warming exceeds anything Earth has previously experienced. When conditions change rapidly, plants and animals may not be able to adapt to the new conditions. Their populations might not be able to spread to other locations in time.

Analysis Questions

1. What are all the different consequences associated with increasing global temperature?

2. What weather changes are anticipated as a result of global climate change? Do scientists expect the same weather changes everywhere? Why?

3. Why are glaciers melting? How do melting glaciers contribute to the effects of global warming on the ocean?

4. How does global climate change affect sea level? What are two causes of this change?

5. How will changes in sea level affect the land? What types of land will be affected? What effect do you predict this will have on human populations?

6. How does global warming lead to more widespread occurrences of some diseases?

7. What changes in wildlife behavior or habitat have been documented and attributed to global warming?

8. Answer the essential question: *How could global warming affect life on Earth?* Answer the question by describing two ways that these effects might change your life or the lives of your children.

Uncertainty in Science

? **Essential Question:** *What is scientific uncertainty? How does it affect how people and governments react to problems like global climate change?*

Uncertainty in Climate Science

The goal of science is to explain the natural world. However, there is no such thing as a certain fact in science. Scientific understanding depends on evidence. The more evidence for a scientific claim, the more it will be believed and accepted as a fact.

The global climate change debate is a good example of the role uncertainty plays in science. In the 1980s, some scientists published articles on the possibility that Earth's average temperatures were increasing. They called it "global warming." They said its cause might be from the burning of fossil fuels. As these fuels burn, the accumulation of heat-trapping greenhouse gases, like carbon dioxide, are released into the atmosphere. At first, it was just a theory. Scientists did not have enough accurate temperature measurements to prove their theory. They needed more measurements from around the world. They also needed temperatures measured over a longer period of time. Scientists could show an increase in atmospheric levels of carbon dioxide over the last century. However, they could not show any certain link between human activities and that rise. Scientists did not understand climate well enough to predict that increased carbon dioxide levels caused global warming.

Global warming remained a very controversial issue for more than a decade. Many scientists disputed the existence of global warming. Others disagreed over its likely effects. However, scientists all over the world were interested in studying the idea. Governments decided to fund scientific investigations on the issue. Scientists started collecting data to develop a better understanding of Earth's climate. Over 25 years, scientists gathered more and more evidence that global warming is occurring. The evidence also showed that it is the direct result of human combustion of fossil fuels.

In 2001, climate scientists from the Intergovernmental Panel on Climate Change (IPCC) issued a report. They said they were now certain that global warming is occurring. They said the cause was a build-up of atmospheric gases from human activities. However, other scientists say there still remains some uncertainty about global warming. (Scientists now prefer to call it global climate change.) Overall, average temperatures on Earth are increasing, but in some places, they are likely to decrease. In many places, changes in temperature will create problems like changing precipitation patterns or ocean levels. Scientists are still debating how much temperatures will change and the effects of those changes.

Scientists are uncertain about global climate change because temperature and precipitation are part of a very complicated system. There are many causes and effects in Earth's climate that scientists do not fully understand. For example, scientists know that as temperatures increase, more water evaporates. They are uncertain about the effects of that increased evaporation.

Water is a greenhouse gas. More water in the atmosphere will increase the heat retention of the atmosphere. This could therefore intensify the Earth's warming effect. More water in the atmosphere is also likely to increase cloud cover. Clouds shade the Earth, reducing the heating effect of the Sun. Scientists are working to increase their understanding of these opposing effects. However, it is still a subject of uncertainty.

Earth's system is like the human body. Scientists understand how many of the individual parts work, but the parts combine in very complex ways. This makes it difficult to understand the effects of specific changes until they happen.

In much of science, scientists understand causes and effects by doing experiments. However, it is much harder for climate scientists to conduct experiments on Earth's climate. Instead, they often use computer models of climate. A computer model is a simulation that represents scientists' best understanding of how a system works. Using a climate model, a scientist can "test" the effect of increasing temperatures on cloud cover. They can also predict how that might effect long-term temperature change. The results of an experiment with a climate model are only as accurate as the model itself. If the climate model is not accurate about the real system, it will not produce accurate predictions.

So, how do scientists test a climate model? They use it to predict the past. Scientists have an accurate record of what has happened in the past. They enter data from the past to see if the model predicts results that agree with the historical record. If it does, they have evidence that their model is accurate. If it doesn't, they know they need to improve their model. Even if a computer model predicts past climate accurately, it still could be wrong about future climate. This is especially so if human activities are creating unique conditions.

Types of Uncertainty in Science

There are several different forms that uncertainty takes in science. One is uncertainty in observations; another is uncertainty about causes and effects.

Uncertainty in observations. Any time a scientist measures a quantity; there is some uncertainty in that measurement. A temperature measurement may be inaccurate by 1 degree, .1 degree, or .01 degree. It depends on the accuracy of the thermometer. No matter how good a measurement device is, it always has some degree of uncertainty. Uncertainty about observations leads scientists to provide *estimates* of accuracy with their measurements. For example, a scientist will report a temperature measurement as being accurate to within .1 degree, if that is the accuracy of his measurement device. In the past, there was significant uncertainty in temperature measurements. However, the technology for measuring climate variables has improved very much over the last 30 years. Scientists now have much more accurate observations of temperature and other climate variables. This means certainty about current climate observations is much higher.

Uncertainty about causes and effects. Scientists develop explanations for how systems work based on their observations. They also try to collect additional evidence for their explanations. An explanation that describes the relationships between cause and effect is often called a *model*. Scientists use their models of causes and effects to predict new observations. They then try to collect new observations in the real world to confirm these predictions. The certainty of a model depends on the observations it is based on and how accurate those observations are. Scientists do lots of different experiments to collect more observations to base their models on. However, if their observations are uncertain, that model will be uncertain.

When a scientist makes a prediction based on a model of cause and effect, it will include the certainty of the model. For example, a scientist might predict that there is a 90% chance that a result will occur. In the past, climate models were not very certain because they were not based on accurate observations. Even with accurate observations, climate is a very complicated system. It is difficult to develop a model that represents all the causes and effects with a high level of certainty. For example, scientists currently predict that average temperatures will rise between 1.4° and 5.8°C between 1990 and 2100. The range of the estimate is so large because scientists have two major sources of uncertainty. One is uncertainty over how emissions of carbon dioxide might change in the next century. The other is uncertainty in the computer models scientists use to make these estimates.

Uncertainty leads to disagreements among scientists. This is a normal part of the scientific process. When scientists disagree, they try to gather evidence for their positions to reduce uncertainty. In the debate over global warming in the 1980s and 1990s, both forms of uncertainty were present. Temperature measurements were uncertain, so scientists disagreed over whether global temperatures were increasing. If they agreed temperatures were increasing, they disagreed by how much. Uncertainty over cause and effect led to disagreements about the likely effects of global warming. Some scientists have argued that there will be large numbers of species extinctions as a result of global climate change. Others have argued that there will be few extinctions. Their observations have led to different conclusions about the causes and effects of species extinction. These disagreements lead scientists to collect more observations to improve their understanding of cause and effect.

Decision-making Under Uncertainty

Scientists accept that uncertainty is a part of science. The goal of science is to increase understanding by reducing uncertainty. Scientists are steadily reducing our uncertainty about global climate change. For example, nearly all climate scientists agree that global climate change is now occurring as a result of human carbon dioxide emissions. However, there is a level of uncertainty about what this will mean for the future. Scientists do not agree on how quickly this climate change will occur or on its effects.

Meanwhile, individuals and governments need to make important decisions about global climate change. Governments are making decisions about whether to try to prevent or reduce global climate change. Global climate change might effect their decisions about what kinds of power plant should be built. It might effect whether to change emission requirements for cars and trucks. Individuals are making decisions about what products to purchase, how much to heat and cool their home, or whether to buy real estate close to sea-level.

When one makes decisions under uncertainty, there are two considerations. How uncertain is the science and how significant are the possible consequences? Suppose an event could have significant, negative outcomes. One might prepare for it even if there is great uncertainty about the likelihood of the event. For example, scientists cannot predict the occurrence of earthquakes very accurately. However, most people who live in an earthquake zone know the effects of an earthquake are severe enough to make preparations. If there is great uncertainty about an event, however, one might choose not to take any action at all, even if it is potentially disastrous, until the certainty increases.

Ever since scientists have been discussing the possibility of global warming, there have been a variety of responses among decision-makers. Those responses have changed as the certainty of the science has changed.

Initially, the science was so uncertain that many people said that it was not worth taking any action. However, others argued that the possible effects of global climate change could be so disastrous that immediate action to prevent it was necessary. As the science of climate change has become more certain, the debate has shifted from whether to take action to what action to take. Some scientists argue that steps should be taken to prevent or reduce global climate change. Others argue that steps should be taken to prepare and adapt to it. Still others argue that the effects are still too uncertain and too far in the future to act upon now.

Decisions that individuals or organizations make based on uncertain science depend on their values. For example, a decision may depend upon how comfortable they are with taking a risk. It may depend on how much they have to lose in the event of a negative outcome. It may depend upon how much faith they have in the ability of future technologies to solve problems. It may depend upon how they balance the importance of human activities against the importance of preserving the natural environment. You will learn more about the processes behind global climate change and its possible effects in this chapter. As you do, pay attention to how certain scientists are about the processes you are studying. At the end of this unit, you will be making a decision about building a new power plant. You will need to consider both the certainty of the science about a power plant's impact on the environment and your own values.

Analysis Questions

1. What caused scientists and governments to become more certain that global climate change is occurring?

2. What are some of the current uncertainties around global climate change? Why are these uncertainties still debated?

3. What are the types of uncertainty in science? Why are they important to identify in scientific investigations?

4. How can two scientists studying the same natural phenomena disagree?

5. What role do models play in understanding climate processes?

6. Answer the essential questions: *What is scientific uncertainty? How does it affect how people and governments react to problems such as global climate change?*

Lesson 2
Earth's Natural Temperature

 Driving Question: *Can we tell that climate change is occurring?*

Overview

If scientists are right about global climate change, Earth's temperature should be slowly rising. Keep in mind though that Earth's temperature is changing all the time. Summers are warmer than winters. We have cold years and warm years. Sometimes, there are floods and sometimes droughts. How can we determine if climate change is occurring with all these variations present? In this lesson, we will examine Earth's temperature over the past 10,000 years. We will investigate whether the recent changes in Earth's temperature are normal variations or something to be concerned about.

Important Content

- Temperature on Earth naturally varies from place to place and moment to moment. This makes it very difficult to detect whether human activities are having an impact on global climate.

- Incoming solar energy and albedo determine the amount of energy that is reflected and absorbed by the Earth. Temperature variations on Earth can be partially explained by differences in albedo on the surface.

Changing Temperature

Essential Question: *Do graphs of temperature change over time provide evidence that the overall temperature of the Earth is warming? Why or why not?*

Overview

To determine if global climate change is occurring, scientists need to know how temperature has changed over time. How do they do this? What type of temperature data do they look at? Do they look at temperature data for 1 month, 1 year, 100 years, 9,500 years? Or do they have to look at temperature changes over even longer time periods?

To understand how scientists approach climate change, you must understand the difference between weather and climate. Weather is the state of the atmosphere at a specific time and place. If rain is predicted for the weekend in Milwaukee, that's considered weather. Changes in weather are short-term, local responses to changes in atmospheric conditions. Climate refers to long-term, average weather conditions for a location. Long-term changes in climate are responses to global conditions. These conditions include solar energy, ocean circulation, and the tilt of the Earth.

In this lesson, you will analyze graphs that show local and global temperature changes. You will distinguish between weather data and climate data. You will also determine if changes in weather are related to changes in climate. This activity will show you that temperatures vary on many different time and geographical scales.

Procedure

Your teacher will assign you one of the following graphs. For your graph, do the following. Be prepared to share your results with the rest of the class.

1. For each graph, identify the following:

    the length of time the graph covers

    the minimum temperature

    the maximum temperature

    the range between the maximum and minimum value

    the biggest difference between two readings that are next to each other

    the smallest difference between two readings that are next to each other

2. Describe the overall line shape or trend shown on the graph.

3. Use the graphs below. Explain why Chicago's range of temperatures changes daily, monthly and seasonally.

4. Answer the essential question: *Do graphs of temperature change over time provide evidence that the overall temperature of the Earth is warming? Why or why not?*

Graph 1

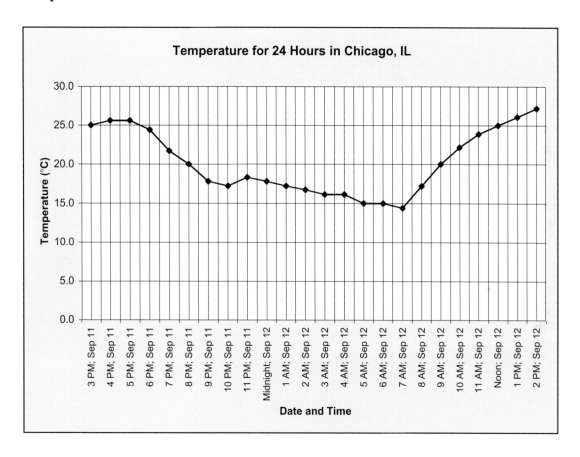

Graph 1: One Day of Temperature

Graph 2

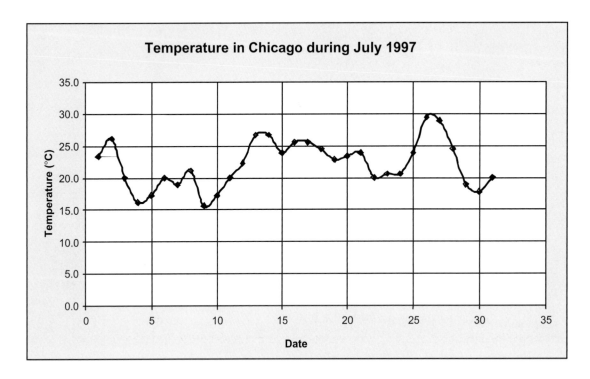

Graph 2: One Month of Temperature

Graph 3

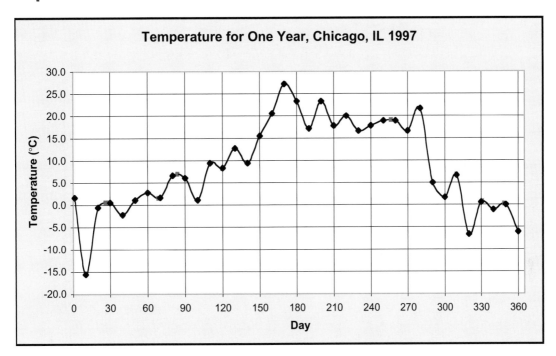

Graph 3: One Year of Temperature (Chicago, IL, 1997)

Graph 4

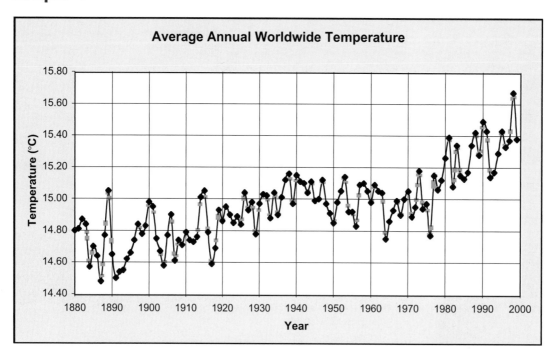

Graph 4: One Century of Temperature (Worldwide)

Graph 5

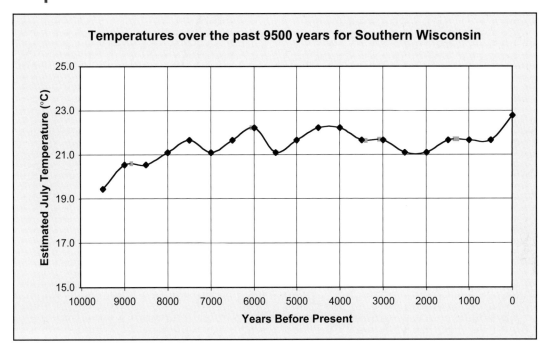

Graph 5: 9500 Years of Temperature Data (from Southern Wisconsin)

Temperature over Time

? ***Essential Question:*** *How does a change in temperature during one day compare to the change in globally averaged temperatures over 50,000 years?*

Overview

In this lesson, you will read about long-term temperature measurements and how scientists study them. You'll also see why small increases in global temperature may have a huge impact on climates around the world.

Temperature over Time

You have learned the difference between climate and weather. There is one very important difference between how scientists view global climate and how we view weather. This difference has to do with the way temperature is measured. Local, weather-related temperature variations can be very high. On a hot summer day in Chicago, the daytime temperature may be 100°F, while the nighttime temperature may dip to 70°F. Extreme temperature variations like this are very common.

When scientists refer to global climate change, they are referring to globally averaged temperature. Globally averaged temperature is the average of the temperatures around the Earth from the North Pole to the South Pole. About 100 years ago, the globally averaged temperature was about 62°F.

The global climate is very sensitive to even small changes in global average temperature. Scientists study ancient climates, paleoclimates, to determine what globally averaged temperatures were at different times in the distant past. This helps them understand how changes in globally averaged temperature affected the land, the oceans, and living things.

Some scientists believe that Earth's climate changes naturally in 100,000-year cycles. These cycles are called "grand climate cycles." A grand climate cycle has two phases: the ice age and the interglacial period. An ice age is a period of time where the globally average temperature decreases. This causes ice sheets to form in non-polar areas. The interglacial phase of the grand climate cycle has a milder climate. Our current climate is considered to be an interglacial period. One grand climate cycle includes one ice age, one warmer interglacial period, and another ice age. Studies have revealed that the difference in globally averaged temperature between the coldest part of an ice age and warmest part of the interglacial period is between 5° and 6°C (about 8° to 11°F). These changes in temperature usually occur soon after the end of the ice age.

Scientists have measured increases since about 1850 in the globally averaged temperature. The most recent studies show that the globally averaged temperature is currently increasing at a rate of 2.5°C (about 4.5°F) per century. This increase in 200 years is equal to a normal cycle increase over 50,000 years. The change in the global average temperature is as large as the temperature shift during the last ice age recovery. However, this change is occurring in only 200 years and it is not due to the ice age cycle.

What will be the effects of this globally averaged temperature increase---equal in magnitude to half a grand climate cycle in just two centuries? The change is so extreme, rapid, and so unprecedented, no one can say for sure. But it is known that the current increase is greater and more rapid than any that has occurred in the last 10,000 years.

Analysis Questions

1. What is globally averaged temperature?

2. What is the difference in globally averaged temperature between the coldest part of an ice age and the warmest part of an interglacial period? How long does it normally take for this temperature change to occur?

3. How quickly are similar changes in globally averaged temperature occurring now?

4. Answer the essential question: *How does a change in temperature during one day compare to the change in global temperatures over 50,000 years?*

Lesson 3
Sunlight and Temperature

Driving Question: *How does temperature work?*

Overview

You have seen how Earth's temperature has changed over time. In this lesson, you will explore what produces different temperatures on Earth. You will start with energy from the Sun and study what happens when it hits the surface of the Earth. You will also use WorldWatcher datasets to see how different areas of the world are affected by the Sun. In the next lesson, you will see how sunlight contributes to Earth's temperatures.

Important Content

- Incoming solar energy and albedo determine the amount of energy that is reflected and absorbed by the Earth. Temperature variations on Earth can be partially explained by differences in albedo of the surface.

Energy From The Sun

Essential Question: *What happens when the Sun's energy hits the Earth?*

Overview

Why do temperatures on Earth change? To answer this, you need to understand how the Earth warms and cools. The energy that heats Earth comes from the Sun. What happens to the Sun's energy once it reaches our planet? There are three things that happen when the energy in sunlight hits an object. (1) The energy can be reflected, or bounce off the object. (2) The energy can be absorbed, transforming light energy into heat energy. (3) The energy can be transmitted, or pass through the object to something else. Often, a combination of these things happens. As you go through this activity, you will be looking at several objects and determining whether sunlight is absorbed, reflected or transmitted. (Remember: our eyes detect light that is reflected off of objects. So anything you can see must have light reflecting off it.)

Materials

- 6" piece of black construction paper
- 6" piece of shiny aluminum foil
- 6" piece of clear plastic wrap
- 100 watt light bulb (optional, as a substitute for the Sun)

Safety

Follow standard safety rules and school safety rules for laboratory activities.

Procedure

1. Hold up the piece of black construction paper. Describe what you see happening to the Sun's energy as it encounters the paper.

2. Repeat with the foil and clear plastic wrap.

Analysis Questions

1. Fill out the following chart using the three things that can happen to the light energy.

	Most of the energy was:	Some of the energy was:	Very little energy was:
Black Paper			
Foil			
Plastic Wrap			

2. Which of the three processes – reflection, transmission, or absorption -- is responsible for the black piece of paper getting warm?

3. What do you think happens (reflection, transmission or absorption) when the Sun hits:

   a. grass

   b. sand

   c. ice

4. Answer the essential question: *What happens when the Sun's energy hits the Earth?*

Sunlight And Groundcover

Essential Question: *What types of groundcover reflect the most light? What types absorb the most light?*

Overview

You have seen how radiant energy (light) behaves when it interacts with matter. The *total* amount of energy reaching an object = the sum of the amount *transmitted* + the amount *absorbed* + the amount *reflected*. In this activity, you will investigate how this equation applies to energy from the Sun (sunlight) as it reaches Earth. You will study how incoming sunlight is reflected or absorbed at the Earth's surface. You will use two different models in this activity. They will help you understand the relationship between the amount of incoming solar energy absorbed at the surface of the Earth and the temperature of the Earth.

Materials

Worldwatcher geographic visualization software

Earth Atmosphere Reflectivity (Clear Sky), April, 1997
File name: **Albedo Clear 04-1987.wwf**
Accessed from energy balance diagram, Earth Atmosphere Reflectivity button

Earth Surface Cover Earth Contemporary
File name: **Earth Surface Cover.wwf**
Accessed from Geography diagram, Surface button

Procedure Part I: Incoming Solar Energy and Reflectivity

1. Launch WorldWatcher and click on the Energy Balance button.

2. Click the **Earth Atmosphere Reflectivity** button. Open the dataset for clear sky in April 1997. You should see a visualization open with the title "**Albedo Clear 4-87**".

3. The darker areas mean less reflectivity and the lighter areas mean more reflectivity. Light blue areas indicate areas for which no data is available. Record the units used in this dataset and what it is measuring.

4. In your notebook, record which parts of Earth reflect the most sunlight and which reflect the least sunlight.

5. Keep "**Albedo (Clear) 4-87**" open. Open the dataset "**Earth Surface Cover.wwf**". Arrange your new visualization alongside your previous visualization for "**Albedo (Clear) 4-87**." Activate the synchronized mouse button in the tool bar.

6. Select all areas within "**Albedo (Clear) 4-87**" that have an albedo of 30% or greater.

7. Record four types of ground cover that are in regions that have an albedo greater than 30%.

8. Clear all selections. In the ground cover dataset, select all regions that are classified as Tundra. Describe the range of the albedo in those regions. Record the average (mean) albedo for Tundra.

9. Repeat Step 8 for the 3 other different types of ground cover you selected previously. Rank your results, so you have a table that describes the groundcovers that have the highest albedo.

10. Select 4 types of ground cover that you think would not reflect much sunlight. Record their average albedo.

Analysis Questions

1. When sunlight hits the Earth, is any of the sunlight energy transmitted by the Earth? Why or why not?

2. Explain why certain types of ground cover are more reflective than others. Use evidence from Lesson 3: *Energy From The Sun* for your answer.

3. Answer the essential question: *What types of groundcover reflect the most light? What types absorb the most light?*

Lesson 4
Predicting Temperatures

Driving Question: *Can you use incoming solar energy and reflectivity to predict Earth temperatures?*

Overview

In this chapter, you will learn about what determines temperatures on Earth. This will help explain why scientists believe burning fossil fuels to generate electricity or fuel our cars may be contributing to global climate change. You have learned how sunlight and the reflectivity of different ground covers affect how different locations on Earth are heated by the Sun. In this lesson, you will use what you have learned to predict temperatures on Earth. You will use a computer model to make these predictions, the way scientists do. You will then compare your predictions to actual surface temperatures.

Important Content

Incoming solar energy and albedo determine the amount of energy that is reflected and absorbed by the Earth. Temperature variations on Earth can be partially explained by differences in albedo on the surface.

Modeling the Earth's Temperature

Essential Question: *How does Earth-atmosphere reflectivity affect temperature on Earth?*

Overview

In this lesson, you will use a computer model to simulate Earth's energy balance. The computer model will calculate how much sunlight is absorbed and reflected by Earth's surface. It will also show how these change when the reflectivity of the Earth changes. The model will calculate a surface temperature based on how much of the Sun's energy is absorbed at the Earth's surface. To make things simpler, the model will "act" as if Earth did not have an atmosphere. Later, you will add the atmosphere to the model.

Materials

computers with "**Simple Reflectivity Model**" installed

Getting Started

To open the model, double-click on the icon labeled, **Simple Reflectivity Model.** Your screen should look like the one on the next page. If you cannot see everything in the picture, click on the lower right-hand corner of the window. Drag it to make the window larger.

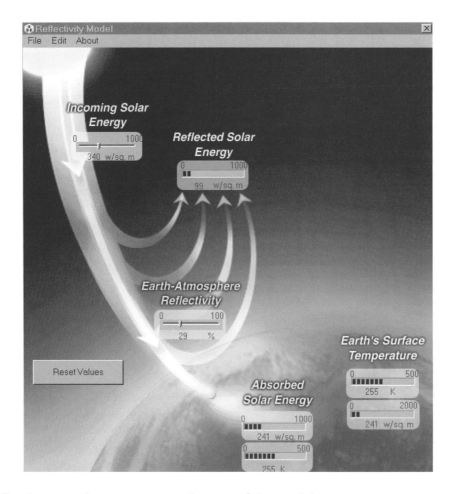

The five icons each represent one element of the model.

Here is how the values in the model are calculated:

Reflected Solar Energy = Incoming Solar Energy Reflectivity

Absorbed Solar Energy = Incoming Solar Energy — Reflected Solar Energy

Each of the arrows you see on the screen indicates a relationship between the elements of the model.

Procedure

1. Open the model and click on the **Reset Values** button. This sets this model to values that most closely resemble actual conditions on Earth.

2. Record what happens to the other four values when incoming solar energy increases. Your response should indicate if the other values increase, decrease, or stay the same.

3. Change the Earth-atmosphere reflectivity to a higher value, 75%. In your notebook, record how the absorbed energy changes when reflectivity changes.

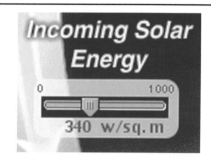	**Incoming Solar Energy** is the amount of sunlight arriving from the Sun. Incoming solar energy is measured in watts, just like a light bulb. Scientists talk about incoming solar energy as the number of watts of energy hitting every square meter of the Earth's surface (watts per meter squared).
	**Earth-Atmosphere Reflectivity** is the fraction of the sunlight that is reflected back out into space by the Earth's surface. If reflectivity equals one quarter (or 0.25) then one-quarter of the sunlight is reflected back into space. Reflectivity is commonly known as albedo.
	**Reflected Solar Energy** is the amount of sunlight that is reflected back into space by the Earth's atmosphere and its surface. The amount of reflected solar energy is calculated by multiplying the incoming solar energy by the reflectivity (albedo).
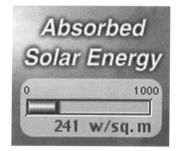	**Absorbed Solar Energy** is the amount of solar energy that is absorbed by the Earth's surface. When the Earth's surface absorbs solar energy, the surface heats up. The absorbed energy is calculated by subtracting the reflected solar energy from the incoming solar energy.
	**Earth's Surface Temperature** is how warm the Earth's surface would be if the only thing heating it up were the absorbed energy from the Sun.

> **Stop and Think**
>
> What happens to absorbed solar energy when reflectivity goes up?
>
> What happens to absorbed solar energy when reflectivity goes down?

4. Describe what happens to reflected solar energy when Earth-atmosphere reflectivity changes.

5. Now look at the Earth's surface temperature box. In your notebook, describe how the surface temperature changes when the reflectivity is changed.

6. You can also change the value of incoming solar energy. Move it up and down and observe what happens as you change it. Describe what happens to the other variables when you change incoming solar energy.

7. Click the **Reset Values** button. Complete the table below, keeping the incoming solar energy constant at 340 w/m2. Change the Earth-atmosphere reflectivity to five different values.

Data Table

Incoming solar energy should be constant at 340 w/m².

Earth-Atmosphere Reflectivity (%)	Absorbed Solar Energy (W/m²)	Reflected Solar Energy (W/m²)	Earth's Surface Temperature (K)
100%			
75%			
50%			
25%			
0%			

Analysis Questions

1. The average reflectivity of Earth's surface is about 20%. Use the model to find the resulting surface temperature.

2. The model reports temperature in degrees Kelvin (K). To convert this to degrees Fahrenheit, use this formula: $F = (1.8 \times K) - 460$. At 20% reflectivity, what is Earth's temperature in degrees Fahrenheit?

3. Is your answer to Question 2 colder or warmer than you thought Earth's actual temperature was? (Remember: this is an average, annual temperature for the whole world.)

4. Is reflectivity constant on Earth's surface?

5. Answer the essential question: *How does Earth-atmosphere reflectivity affect temperature on Earth?*

What Should The Earth's Temperature Be?

Essential Question: *Is Earth's surface temperature only due to incoming solar energy?*

Overview

In Lesson 4: *Modeling the Earth's Temperature*, you explored how temperature on Earth would change if albedo (reflectivity) changed. Now, you will use WorldWatcher to see what Earth's temperature should be based on incoming solar energy and the actual albedo of the Earth. Pay attention to the temperature results you get. You might be surprised by how cold the Earth should be!

Materials

WorldWatcher geographic visualization software

Dataset: Absorbed Solar Energy, March 1987
File Name: **Absorbed Solar Clear 03-87.wwf**
Location: Energy Balance, under Absorbed Solar Energy

Dataset: Actual Surface Temperature, March 1987
File Name: **Surface Temperature 03-1987.wwf**
Location: Energy Balance, under Surface Temperatures

Procedure

1. Open WorldWatcher. Open the dataset that shows absorbed solar energy for March 1997. This visualization shows the average amount of solar energy absorbed by the Earth and atmosphere during that month. (It's in the **Energy Balance** section, under **Absorbed Solar Energy**.)

2. Click on the **Window Math Operation** button in the toolbar (or select window math from the "Analysis" menu). Choose **Convert to temperature** as the math operation at the top of the window. This calculates the temperature you would expect Earth to be as a result of absorbing the amount of energy in the original visualization. Click **OK**.

3. The resulting image will display temperature in degrees Kelvin (K). To change the temperature back to Fahrenheit degrees, select the **Appearance** menu and choose **Units**. Click on **Use alternative units.**

4. Add a country overlay by going to the display menu and choosing overlay and country.

5. Adjust the colorscheme of your new picture so that it is clear where the average temperature would be below freezing. Go to the **Appearance** menu and select **Colorscheme**. Select the color set called "Rainbow (divided)." Set the "lower limit" to -48 degrees F and the "upper limit" to 112 degrees F. This should give you a clear division between green and yellow at freezing (32 degrees F). Click **OK**.

6. Save the visualization according to your teacher's instructions. Name it **AbsorbedTemp.wwf.**

Stop and Think

What is the temperature that this visualization shows for your home town? Is your home town really that cold in March?

---

7. Compare your **AbsorbedTemp.wwf** to actual temperatures. Open the visualization for the surface temperature 3/87 dataset.

8. Place the two visualizations side by side. Record the similarities and differences.

9. Use the window math button to subtract **AbsorbedTemp.wwf** from **Surface Temperature 3/87**. Describe what this visualization represents.

10. Save the visualization. Name it **TemperatureDifference.wwf**.

Analysis Questions

1. Look at the visualization you made in Step 6 named **AbsorbedTemp.wwf**. This visualization shows the temperature of Earth based only on absorbed energy from the Sun. If the world were really like this, where would the most desirable places be for people to live?

2. List as many conclusions as you can about how life on Earth would be different under these climate conditions.

3. Look at the visualization you made in Step 10, called **TemperatureDifference.wwf**. This visualization shows the difference between the actual temperature and the temperature based only on absorbed solar energy. What might be causing the Earth to be warmer?

4. Answer the essential question: *Is Earth's surface temperature only due to incoming solar energy? Use evidence to support your answer.*

Ocean Circulation, Albedo, and Temperature

? *Essential Question: How could ocean circulation and albedo combine to turn warming into cooling?*

Overview

The last two lessons showed how the Earth's albedo and incoming solar energy work together to influence Earth's temperature. In the next chapter, you will learn about the influence of the atmosphere on the temperatures we experience. However, there is another very important influence on temperature—the oceans. In this lesson, you will read about how the ocean currents influence air temperatures. You will also learn about a surprising possible result of global warming. Scientists believe that the changes in ocean circulation from global warming could lead to cooling in some places on Earth.

Ocean Circulation and Temperature

Oceans transport huge amounts of heat all around the Earth. Scientists use the phrase "oceanic conveyor belt" to describe the complex process. In this reading, we will focus on one part of this process which transports water through the Atlantic Ocean. It is called the North Atlantic Deep Water (NADW) circulation.

The NADW is a mass of water traveling deep below the Atlantic Ocean's surface. This massive ocean current is formed in the Labrador Sea (northeast of Iceland). It travels southward down the eastern coast of Canada and the United States. It then moves east, away from the coast line, to continue south to the eastern tip of South America. This water mass travels north up the east coast of North America toward northwestern Europe at the ocean's surface. The part of this current that flows in the Atlantic Ocean off North America is called the Gulf Stream. The Gulf Stream flows from the warm waters of the equator and the Caribbean. It carries enormous amounts of heat up the eastern coast of North America to northwestern Europe. The Gulf Stream is one of the reasons why Britain has such a mild climate relative to its latitude. England and Scotland's latitude are about the same as that of central Quebec, Canada. However, while Quebec is frozen solid during the winter, the Gulf Stream keeps Britain fairly warm and often snow-free.

The engine that drives the NADW current is located in the far North Atlantic, north of Greenland and Iceland. Here, the water is extremely cold and contains more salt (about 7% more) than the rest of the ocean. The seawater is very salty because of the cold temperatures and dry climate in the Polar Regions. Because of the cold climate, water at the surface freezes to form icebergs. Due to the dryness of this polar climate, water will evaporate from the oceans, despite the cold air temperatures. When water freezes or evaporates out of the ocean, the salt is left. This makes the seawater saltier, or more saline, than the water elsewhere in the global ocean. Its cold temperature and higher salt content makes this North Atlantic water very dense. Because it is so dense, this cold, salty water sinks toward the ocean bottom. The rotation of the Earth causes this huge, sunken current to begin flowing south toward the equator. As it flows south, the current pushes vast amounts of water ahead of it. This driving of North Atlantic waters southward is the engine moving the NADW.

As this cold, dense water flows south in the ocean's depths, warmer, less dense water flows north to take its place. The cold water moving south begins to warm up from the Sun and contact with warm water. As the cold water warms, the increasing rainfall of the tropics dilutes it. This causes the concentration of salt in the water to decrease. The increased temperature and dilution of the salt causes the seawater to become less dense and rise to the surface of the ocean. The warm current flows along the equator and through the Caribbean, gaining heat. It begins to move northward to fill in behind the cold dense water that is starting to flow south from the North Atlantic. It carries that heat northward to northwestern Europe. The warm ocean current transfers its heat to the continents and local atmosphere of the temperate climate. The current once again becomes dense and salty, and the cycle continues.

Climate Change and the NADW Circulation

The NADW functions only because the waters in the far North Atlantic are so cold and salty. Scientists have considered how the warming temperatures would affect ocean circulation. They expect several changes as a result of the warming of the North Atlantic. First, they expect water in the North Atlantic to retain more of its heat because there will be less conduction of heat to the air. Second, they expect increased precipitation directly into the oceans and run-off from land into the ocean. Third, warmer temperatures are already causing polar ice and glaciers in Greenland to melt. Scientists have seen increased rainfall and higher freshwater input into the North Atlantic. This has reduced the salt content of the waters that form the "engine" of the NADW. The result of increased temperatures and increased salt content are that the North Atlantic water will be less dense. If it is less dense, it will not sink as deeply and will not push the NADW circulation as forcefully.

If the waters of the North Atlantic become less dense, the whole NADW circulation will become weaker. The unusual effect will be that northwestern Europe will begin to cool, rather than continue to warm. If less water is pushed southward, the northward flow of the Gulf Stream will be weakened as well. A weakened Gulf Stream will carry less warmth to northwestern Europe. Scientists believe that weakening the Gulf Stream could reduce the amount of global warming experienced in Europe in the future.

Interaction between Ocean Circulation and Albedo

Some scientists believe that the weakening of the NADW circulation could trigger an ice age. Here's how that could happen. As the Gulf Stream weakens, summers in far northern Europe would get colder because the weakened Gulf Stream would be carrying less heat. In just a few years, areas where snow and ice once melted during the summer will remain covered with snow and ice. Winter will than come again and add more snow and ice. The next summer, the area of snow cover has been expanded. Snow has very high albedo, causing 60% to 90% of the incoming solar radiation to be reflected. The snow-covered areas will not get as much warmth because less solar radiation is absorbed at the Earth's surface. This allows the snow cover to persist, leading to even more snow cover the next year. The area of high albedo (high reflectivity) expands. This further reduces the amount of solar radiation and heat the land absorbs. So even if some summer days are warm, the Earth does not absorb enough heat to melt the snow.

Once this process begins, it generates a "positive feedback" loop. A little summer snow reflects heat. This leads to more snow accumulating, which reflects away even more heat, and so on. Once the albedo effect begins acting, year-by-year, the area covered by year-round snow and ice expands. The albedo effect is very powerful. Scientists have evidence that it requires only one or two decades of snow not melting in northern Europe for an ice age to begin.

Scientists know that the global oceanic conveyor belt has weakened. It might have even stopped completely. They have evidence that the collapse of the oceanic conveyor belt has led to the beginning of ice ages. The fascinating part of this process is that warming of the atmosphere and oceans could trigger dramatic cooling. It shows the complicated relationships between air, land, and water. It also shows how one kind of change in some locations can have very different effects in others.

Scientists believe that weakening of the oceanic conveyor belt could cause cooling in Europe and elsewhere in the future. However, most do not believe that this cooling could trigger an ice age. They believe that the overall warming effect of the build up of heat-trapping gases would prevent an ice age from occurring.

Analysis Questions

1. What is the oceanic conveyor belt circulation? How does it keep northwestern Europe relatively warm?

2. What characteristics does the water have in the area where NADW originates---in the region of the "engine" that powers it?

3. What could cause the oceanic conveyor belt to weaken? What effect would this have on the climate of northwestern Europe?

4. What is the role of albedo in the ice ages that originate in northwestern Europe? Create a flow chart. Show the "positive feedback" loop that results once the albedo of this region increases.

5. Answer the essential question: *How could ocean circulation and albedo combine to turn heating into cooling?*

Lesson 5
Greenhouse Effect

 Driving Question: *How does the atmosphere keep the Earth warm?*

Overview

In Lesson 4, you learned that solar energy is not enough to explain how warm Earth's temperature actually is. In this lesson, you will explore the atmosphere to see what effect it has on Earth's temperature. You will do an experiment to see how different gases in the atmosphere hold heat near the surface of the planet. You will then look at another computer model to explore how the atmosphere keeps the Earth warm.

Important Content

*   The carbon cycle shows how carbon dioxide cycles in and out of the atmosphere. Carbon dioxide, along with other greenhouse gases, could be the cause of a predicted change in Earth's climate.

Global Climate Change

Atmospheric Gases

? ***Essential Question:*** *How would increasing the amount of greenhouse gases in Earth's atmosphere affect Earth's temperature?*

Overview

If solar energy isn't enough to explain how warm Earth is, where does it get its additional heat? Only about 1/2 of the light from the Sun is usually transmitted through the atmosphere and reaches Earth's surface. The other half is either reflected or absorbed by the atmosphere. What else is happening in the atmosphere? When the Earth heats up (from the energy in sunlight), it radiates that heat. This is the same way all hot things warm the air around them. The particles and gases in the atmosphere absorb the infrared energy and radiate it both upward and downward. Much of the energy is emitted back toward Earth's surface.

In today's lab, you will be looking at the heat-absorbing ability of two gases. These gases are commonly found in the atmosphere and absorb long-wave or infrared radiation. Your focus in this lab is to compare the heat-absorbing ability of two atmospheric gases (carbon dioxide and air). You will assume that lamp in your experiment represents the sun. The gases in the atmosphere and also the earth absorb the energy from this lamp. The black paper on the bottom of each of the beakers represents the earth. Like the earth, they will radiate infrared energy. Similar to the Earth's atmosphere, each of the beakers contains one of the heat-absorbing gases. One beaker will contain air and the other beaker carbon dioxide. As the earth (the black paper) and the gases (air and carbon dioxide) absorb energy, they will also radiate energy. The question you need to figure out is which of these gases absorbs and radiates more energy? And how do these heat-absorbing gases affect the temperature on Earth?

Materials

50 mL of Vinegar

12 grams of Baking Soda

2 Erlenmeyer flasks (250-ml)

2 one-hole stoppers

2 bent glass tubes

2 straight glass tubes

2 rubber tubes

Plastic wrap

2 beakers (400 ml)

2 thermometers

Thermometer clamps or tape

Shiny black discs to place in the bottom of the beaker (eg. black paper plates or construction paper)

Heat lamp w/120 W reflector bulb

(Optional) stopwatch

Safety

Follow standard safety rules and school safety rules for laboratory activities.

> **Warning!**
>
> This activity involves materials, which can be considered dangerous. Be sure to follow all safety instructions from your teacher.

Procedure

1. Place the two thermometers into the cup of lukewarm tap water until all read the same temperature. This is to make sure all the thermometers are starting at room temperature.

2. Set up the apparatus by:

Constructing the Carbon Dioxide Collection containers

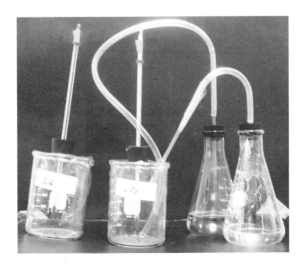

a. Gently push a glass bend in the whole of the one-whole stopper.

b. Attach one of the pieces of rubber tubing to the end of the glass bend that will be on the outside of the Erlenmeyer flask.

c. Place the stopper with the glass bend and rubber tubing on an Erlenmeyer flask.

d. Repeat so that you have two collection containers.

Construction of the Sun, Earth and Atmosphere Model

a. Cut out two pieces of black paper the size of the bottom of the beaker and place the black paper in the bottom of each of the beakers.

b. Attach a thermometer to the inside of each beaker. You may use tape or a thermometer clip if needed. It is important that the bulb of the thermometer is near the bottom but does not touch the side of the beaker or the black paper on the bottom. You want your thermometer to have an accurate measurement of the gases that will be inside the beaker.

c. lace labels either on the beakers or next to the beakers. Label one beaker air and the other carbon dioxide.

d. Place the infrared light 25 cm directly over the two beakers. Make sure the pool of light is equal between the two beakers. DO NOT TURN ON THE LIGHT!

e. Position the two Erlenmeyer flasks next to the beaker you labeled carbon dioxide. Take the free ends of the plastic tubing for each Erlenmeyer flask and place both inside the carbon dioxide beaker. When you begin to make the carbon dioxide, it will leave the Erlenmeyer flask through the plastic tubing and end up inside the carbon dioxide beaker.

f. Measure 6 g of baking soda into each 250 ml Erlenmeyer flask. Measure out 50 mL of vinegar for each 250 ml Erlenmeyer flask.

3. Create a table with "Time," "Temperature of Air," "Temperature of CO_2," as the headers.

Time	Temperature of Air	Temperature of CO_2

TimeTemperature of AirTemperature of CO_2

4. Record the initial temperature (at a time 0 minutes) to the nearest 0.1 degree C for each thermometer.

5. Create the carbon dioxide by dumping 6 g of baking soda in each Erlenmeyer flask followed by 50 mL of vinegar and quickly stopper the flask. Do one first……then turn the lamp on…….then do the second.

6. Immediately turn on the infrared lamp and start timing. After exactly one minute, read the temperature as quickly as possible and record the temperatures.

7. (Optional) After allowing the reaction to occur for a few seconds, use a match or a wooden ember to verify that the beaker is full of carbon dioxide. (The flame will go out when lowered to the level of CO_2).

8. Read and record the temperature every minute for 10 minutes.

9. Make a graph of the "Temperature versus Time" for each gas. Plot time on the x-axis and temperature on the y-axis.

Analysis Questions

1. What source of infrared light does the lamp represent?

2. If the lamp represents the sun (radiating heat) and the gas represents the atmosphere, what is the thermometer measuring?

3. Which atmosphere would be warmer, one comprised of CO_2 or Air? Why?

4. Which is a better absorber of infrared wavelengths, carbon dioxide or air? If so, what is your evidence?

5. Answer the essential question: *How would increasing the amount of greenhouse gases in Earth's atmosphere affect Earth's temperature?*

Greenhouse Effect

? ***Essential Question:*** *What is the atmospheric greenhouse effect and how does it affect temperatures on Earth?*

Procedure

Read the following article about greenhouse effect. Answer the analysis questions.

What is the Greenhouse Effect?

If you have ever been in a greenhouse, you probably noticed that it was warmer inside than it was outside. The "greenhouse effect" refers to the fact that temperatures we feel on Earth are warmer than they would be if the atmosphere didn't exist.

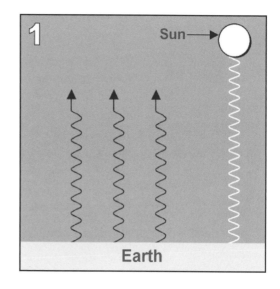

The term "greenhouse effect" is very popular but not very accurate. The process that keeps the inside of a greenhouse warm is very different from the effect of Earth's atmosphere on temperature. Greenhouses maintain their temperatures by keeping the warmed-up air inside them from being released. The radiation from the Sun passes through the glass walls of a greenhouse and warms up the air and objects inside. The glass walls of the greenhouse prevent this mass of warmed-up air from leaving, keeping the inside of the greenhouse warm. The atmospheric greenhouse effect works in a very different way. To understand how it works, you need to know a few basic facts.

First, all objects emit electromagnetic radiation like X-rays, visible light, or infrared radiation. The amount of radiation an object emits depends on its temperature. You can think of temperature as a measure of how much energy the object contains. Hot objects emit more energy than cold objects, but they both emit some energy.

Second, all objects absorb or reflect electromagnetic radiation (energy) when it reaches them. When an object reflects radiation, the radiation does not affect the object. You saw an example of this when you studied the effect of sunlight on highly reflective objects. However, when an object absorbs radiation (energy), the object is affected by the radiation. The most common effect of absorbing energy on an object is it warms up. When the object warms up, it will emit radiation, usually in the form of heat. The hotter the object becomes, the more radiation it will emit. However, objects don't just heat up when they absorb radiation. They can also convert the absorbed energy into another kind of energy. For example, when water evaporates, it converts absorbed energy into mechanical energy. When plants perform photosynthesis, they convert solar energy into chemical energy.

Third, all electromagnetic energy (radiation) has a property called its wavelength. We are all familiar with wavelengths of radiation in visible light. For example, the color red has a longer wavelength and the color blue has a shorter wavelength. We are able to see differences in wavelength as differences in color. Hotter objects radiate at shorter wavelengths than cooler objects. Different objects reflect and absorb light of different wavelengths, depending on their molecular properties.

The sun is a very hot object. It emits an enormous amount of radiation that is primarily shortwave radiation. When this radiation reaches Earth's surface, it is either reflected or absorbed. It depends on the material it strikes and the angle at which the sunlight strikes it.

Absorbed radiation heats Earth's surface. Because Earth's surface is relatively cool, the radiation it emits is mostly longwave (infrared) radiation. In Diagram 1, shortwave solar radiation is shown in white, longwave radiation in black (ignoring reflection).

There is no atmosphere in this diagram, so the longwave radiation escapes directly out into space. Assume that none of the energy is converted into other forms of energy. The amount leaving will be exactly the same as the amount that came from the Sun. On an Earth with no atmosphere, it would be extremely hot during the day and extremely cold at night. This is exactly the case on the Moon, which has no atmosphere.

Earth does have an atmosphere. The molecules in the atmosphere reflect or absorb some of the energy from the Sun. However, a great deal of the solar energy passes through the atmosphere and reaches the Earth's surface. As in Diagram 1, the energy that passes through the atmosphere heats the Earth's surface. The surface then emits longwave radiation upward. However, the atmosphere prevents some of the energy from escaping directly into space. This is the cause of the atmospheric greenhouse effect.

Earth's atmosphere contains certain gases that absorb the longwave radiation emitted by the Earth's surface. These gases are called "greenhouse gases." They heat up and emit longwave radiation themselves, as in Diagrams 2 and 3. Greenhouse gases are more efficient at absorbing longwave radiation than other gases. The main greenhouse gases are water vapor (H_2O), carbon dioxide (CO_2), methane (CH_4), ozone (O_3), and chlorofluorocarbons (CFCs).

Diagrams 2 and 3 show that after absorbing longwave radiation from Earth, the greenhouse gases re-emit that energy. Some of that radiation goes out to space, some stays in the atmosphere, and some settles back toward Earth's surface.

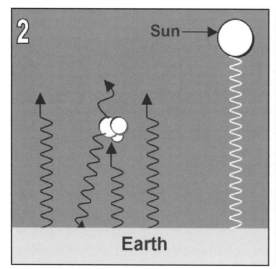
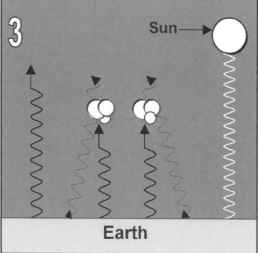

In the atmospheric greenhouse effect, each greenhouse gas molecule acts as a heat source. Part of what we feel as warm temperature comes from these gas molecules. In fact, Earth's surface gets about twice as much energy from the atmosphere as it does from the Sun. This is because the Sun is very hot, but it covers only a small part of the daytime sky. The atmosphere is all around us all the time. So Earth has two heat sources---the Sun and the greenhouse gases in the atmosphere. This makes temperatures at Earth's surface almost 34°C (60°F) warmer than they would be without an atmosphere.

The greenhouse effect is a natural process. Without the greenhouse effect, Earth's surface would be too cold for life as we know it to exist. However, human activities are causing an unnatural increase in the amount of greenhouse gases in our atmosphere. As these greenhouse gases build up, they increase the heat-trapping greenhouse effect. Scientists believe this is contributing to global climate change.

The Most Important Greenhouse Gas: Water

Carbon dioxide, methane, and CFC's are the greenhouse gases that receive most of the attention in the popular press. However, water vapor is the most significant greenhouse gas. Scientists estimate that water vapor is responsible for as much as 60-70% of the total atmospheric greenhouse effect on clear, sunny days.

Water vapor probably plays a particularly important role in global climate change. This is because any increase in warming is expected to increase the amount of water vapor in the atmosphere. Warmer temperatures increase evaporation from the Earth's surface and allow the atmosphere to retain more water vapor. Water vapor is an effective greenhouse gas. A build-up of water vapor in the atmosphere will increase the greenhouse effect. This cycle of increasing temperatures, leading to increasing water vapor, leading to increasing greenhouse effect, and even higher temperatures is called a *positive feedback cycle*. (This feedback accompanies cooling as well.) Scientists believe this cycle between warming and water vapor increases the effects of other greenhouse gases. The effect of an increase in carbon dioxide in the atmosphere could be multiplied by the resulting increase in water vapor.

Analysis Questions

1. Explain how molecules in the atmosphere create the atmospheric greenhouse effect.

2. What naturally-occurring gases in the atmosphere produce Earth's greenhouse effect?

3. How are people today adding to the atmosphere's greenhouse effect?

4. Describe the water vapor feedback cycle during climate warming. What would happen to the concentration of water vapor in the air? What about the temperature?

5. Answer the essential question: *What is the greenhouse effect and how does it affect temperatures on Earth?*

Modeling The Greenhouse Effect

? **Essential Question:** *Will increasing CO_2 in the atmosphere cause temperatures to rise?*

The Controls on Global Climate

There are three important reasons for variations in globally averaged temperatures on Earth. They are: 1) differences in concentrations of greenhouse gases in the atmosphere, 2) variation in the amount of incoming solar energy, and 3) changes in Earth's orbit. We only have the ability to control one of these, the amount of greenhouse gases in the atmosphere. To fully understand global climate change, it is important to look at the natural variations that occur within our climate.

Variations in solar energy

In 2000, scientists noticed that the Sun had reached its solar maximum. This is the time when the Sun's solar radiation is at its greatest. This phenomenon occurs about once every 11 years. This increase in solar radiation has probably contributed to some of the observed global temperature warming. Scientists disagree about exactly how much. Some estimate that only about one-third of the observed warming is caused by increased solar radiation.

Variations in Earth's orbit

Small variations in Earth's orbit around the Sun have been observed over history. It was first noticed thousands of years ago in ancient Greece. In recent years, the variations have been studied closely. This has resulted in the Milankovitch theory. The theory states that there are three causes of Earth's orbit to vary. They are: the wobble of Earth's axis, any slight change in Earth's tilt, and how close its orbit comes to being a circle. The combination of these variations affects the amount of incoming solar radiation and the length of our seasons. Earth's ice ages are caused by the advance and retreat of its ice sheets. Scientists have linked these movements to the periodic variations in Earth's orbit.

Overview

Changes in the amount of solar energy and Earth's orbit have an effect on climate and global temperature. There are, however, other factors to consider when studying global climate change. One is the concentration of greenhouse gases (CO_2 , CH_4 , water vapor, etc.) in the atmosphere.

You have learned that some greenhouse gases, like carbon dioxide and methane, absorb more heat energy then air. Therefore, increasing the amount of carbon dioxide or methane in the atmosphere will increase the greenhouse effect. These gases hold heat near the surface of the Earth instead of allowing it to escape into space.

In Lesson 4: *Modeling the Earth's Temperature*, you used the Simple Reflectivity Model to study temperatures on Earth. In this lesson, you will use a new version of the model with factors for the atmosphere included.

Materials

Full Reflectivity Model

Getting Started

To open the model, double-click on the icon labeled, **Full Reflectivity Model**. Your screen should look like the one below. If you cannot see everything in the picture below, click on the lower right-hand corner of the window. Then drag it to make the window larger.

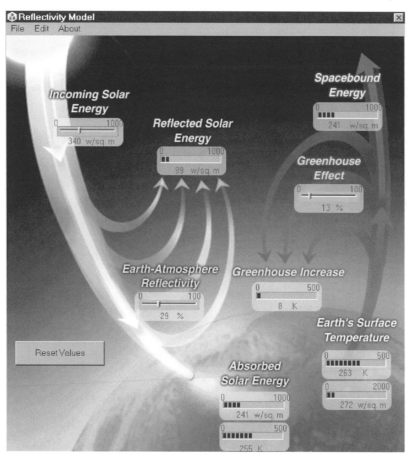

The eight icons each represent one element of the model. They are described below.

	**Incoming Solar Energy** is the amount of sunlight arriving from the Sun. Incoming solar energy is measured in watts, just like a light bulb. Scientists talk about incoming solar energy as the number of watts of energy hitting every square meter of the Earth's surface (watts per meter squared).
	**Earth-Atmosphere Reflectivity** is the fraction of the sunlight that is reflected back out into space by the Earth's surface. If reflectivity equals one quarter (or 0.25) then one-quarter of the sunlight is reflected back into space. Reflectivity is commonly known as albedo.
	**Reflected Solar Energy** is the amount of sunlight that is reflected back into space by the Earth's atmosphere and its surface. The amount of reflected solar energy is calculated by multiplying the incoming solar energy by the reflectivity (albedo).
	**Absorbed Solar Energy** is the amount of solar energy that is absorbed by the Earth's surface. When the Earth's surface absorbs solar energy, the surface heats up. The absorbed energy is calculated by subtracting the reflected solar energy from the incoming solar energy.
	**Earth's Surface Temperature** is how warm the Earth's surface would be if the only thing heating it up were the absorbed energy from the Sun.

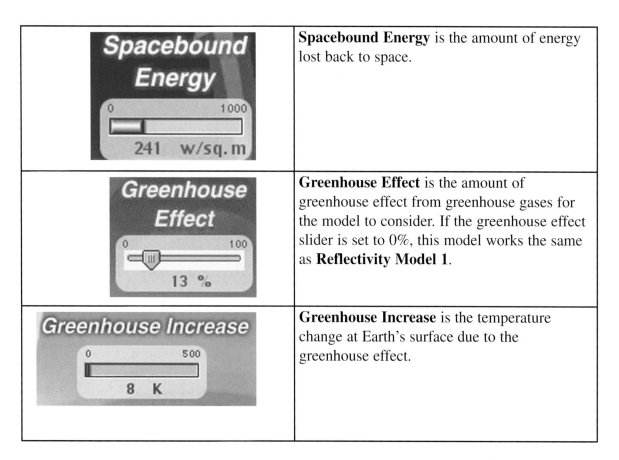

Spacebound Energy	**Spacebound Energy** is the amount of energy lost back to space.
Greenhouse Effect	**Greenhouse Effect** is the amount of greenhouse effect from greenhouse gases for the model to consider. If the greenhouse effect slider is set to 0%, this model works the same as **Reflectivity Model 1**.
Greenhouse Increase	**Greenhouse Increase** is the temperature change at Earth's surface due to the greenhouse effect.

Procedure

1. Click the **Reset Values** button to set the values to normal Earth conditions.

2. When the incoming solar energy slider is changed, what other values change? How?

3. When the earth-atmosphere reflectivity slider is changed, what other values change? How?

4. Describe what happens to the surface temperature when the greenhouse effect goes up.

5. How much does the surface temperature change on Earth when the magnitude of the greenhouse effect doubles?

6. Describe what happens when the carbon dioxide level goes down. (Which variable will change when carbon dioxide level changes?)

7. Make a list of the components of the model that change when carbon dioxide level changes. Explain why you think each one is changing.

8. If the temperature goes up because of greenhouse effect, can you make it go back down by changing something else? What can you change to make the temperature go back down? Describe the conditions that make this possible.

Global Climate Change

Analysis Questions

1. What are the three major factors that control Earth's climate?

2. Why is it so important to learn about greenhouse gases?

3. What does your model predict will happen if the magnitude of the greenhouse effect increases?

4. Do you believe the model? Why or why not?

5. Is there a way to test the model to see if it is accurate?

6. How does the model predict that Earth's temperature will change if the albedo increases? Decreases?

7. Answer the essential question: *Will increasing CO_2 in the atmosphere cause temperatures to rise?*

Measuring Climate Change

 Essential Question: What sources of information do scientists use to understand past climates?

Procedure

Read the following passage. Answer the analysis questions.

Climate Archives

Scientists have been studying changes in climate for a long time. They have not, however, always had written records describing past climate variables, like temperature and precipitation. Written records about the climate exist only since the 18th century. That is not long in comparison with the 4.6 billion-year age of the Earth. Fortunately, the record of Earth's climate for most of this history is preserved in different kinds of climate archives. Scientists use various analytical methods to reconstruct climate of the past. Major climate archives include sedimentary rocks, ice, corals, and tree rings.

Sedimentary Rocks

Sedimentary rocks are a source of climatic information because they record Earth's water cycle. For example, the formation of coals and other minerals called evaporites is related to precipitation and evaporation. Periods of Earth's history when precipitation exceeded evaporation led to the formation of coal. During very dry times, deposits of evaporites such as gypsum and halite were more abundant. By studying how these materials have built up over time, scientists reconstruct changes between more humid and more arid periods. However, these climate records are not perfect. Even though sedimentary rocks date back 4 billion years, they can erode at any time after being deposited. They may also be difficult to date precisely, resulting in an uncertain climate record. Often, the climate record in sedimentary rocks only provides information about intervals of millions of years or more.

Glacial Ice

It is very cold in Earth's polar regions and high mountain tops. As a result, thick sheets of ice often accumulate there over time. Small bubbles of gas may be trapped within the ice and preserved for scientists to study. These gas bubbles are samples of ancient atmospheres. Scientists analyze their composition and reconstruct changes in levels of carbon dioxide and methane in the atmosphere. These gases play an important role in the atmospheric greenhouse effect. Scientists distinguish cooler periods from warmer ones by measuring how much of these greenhouse gases were in the atmosphere during different time periods. Ice usually accumulates in annual layers that form distinct bands. It is fairly easy to determine the age of the gas bubbles by counting the annual layers. Glacial ice has two problems as a climate archive, however. It is restricted to certain, very cold regions and it cannot withstand warmer periods. The glaciers in Greenland and Antarctica contain ice with a maximum age of 400,000 years. Mountain ice preserves a record that does not exceed 10,000 years in age. Thus, the climate archive recorded in glacial ice carries information about smaller intervals than sedimentary rocks, but the record does not go back nearly as far.

Other Climate Archives

You probably know that the wood inside a tree trunk contains many rings. Like the annual layers of glacial ice, each of these rings takes a year to form. Thus, trees contain a history that is easy to read. In addition, the character of the rings (eg. thickness) relate to changes in precipitation. Annual rings are best developed in regions with large differences between seasons. They record changes in precipitation back hundreds, even thousands, of years. Chemical analyses of the wood along with the thickness of the rings also help scientists learn about past climate.

Corals occur in sunny, shallow ocean waters in a narrow belt around the equator. The organisms that build coral reefs put calcium carbonate into the annual bands of their shells. Like tree rings and glacial ice, these bands provide a built-in time scale. Scientists conduct chemical analyses of the calcium carbonate in the coral. The analyses reveal changes in sea surface temperatures as far back as thousands of years.

What does the climate record tell us about current climate change?

Climate scientists have combined data from all these archives. It has allowed them to understand a great deal about the climate of the past. We now know that Earth has experienced extreme variations of climate in the past. Scientists have found evidence for major ice ages; warm, moist "greenhouse" periods; and everything in between. If climate has varied so dramatically in the past, what is so different about the current global climate change? The difference is in the current speed of change. Scientists believe that greenhouse gas concentrations in the atmosphere are increasing 4 to 16 times faster than at any time in recent history. This means that temperatures are likely to increase faster than they have in the past. If that is true, scientists cannot use evidence from past climate change to predict the effects of future climate change.

Analysis Questions

1. What are the benefits of sediment as a climate archive? What are the shortcomings?

2. What are the benefits of glacial ice as a climate archive? What are the shortcomings?

3. What are the benefits of the other climate archives? What are their shortcomings?

4. How far back can we use each of the archives to learn about past climate?

5. What does the climate record tell us about the differences between current climate change and climate change in the past?

6. Answer the essential question: *What sources of information do scientists use to understand past climates?*

Lesson 6
Carbon Dioxide

 Driving Question: *What is carbon dioxide's role in the greenhouse effect? In global warming?*

Overview

So far, you've read about the greenhouse effect and global warming. You have also learned about the consequences they might have. In this lesson, you'll explore the role carbon dioxide plays in the greenhouse effect by studying the natural carbon cycle. You will look at graphs that relate the temperature on Earth to carbon dioxide levels in the atmosphere. You will look at the human activities that affect the carbon cycle. Finally, you will determine the impact those activities might have on the natural greenhouse effect.

Important Content

- The global carbon cycle shows how carbon dioxide cycles in and out of the atmosphere. Carbon dioxide, along with other greenhouse gases, could be the cause of a change in Earth's climate.

- Many everyday human activities can contribute to global climate change.

- Decisions about how our electricity is generated could have a large effect on questions about climate change.

Temperature and Carbon Dioxide

? ***Essential Question:*** *How does the amount of carbon dioxide in the atmosphere relate to temperature?*

Overview

Evidence shows that carbon dioxide (CO_2) levels in the atmosphere have greatly increased over the last 100 years. Global temperatures have also increased over this period, but not as consistently. Are these increases linked to each other or just a coincidence?

Nearly all scientists agree that humans are causing globally averaged temperature to increase. They say the increase is caused by releasing huge amounts of CO_2 into the atmosphere by burning fossil fuels. A small group of scientists disagree. They say there is not enough data to prove with certainty that human actions are causing global temperature increases. These scientists believe that the observed increases could be caused by natural processes. Let's look at some of the data to understand the relationship between human emissions of carbon dioxide and global temperature. This is the most hotly debated aspect of climate change.

Procedure

Look at the graphs. Answer the following analysis questions.

Analysis Questions

1. What variables are shown in these graphs? What relationship, if any, do you observe between the two variables?

2. Look back at the graphs of temperature variation in Lesson 2: *Changing Temperature*. Use what you have observed in this lesson. Write a paragraph explaining whether an increase in CO_2 levels explains the apparent increase in globally averaged temperature over the last century.

3. What is at least one other possible explanation, besides CO_2, for the temperature increases over the last 100 years?

4. Answer the essential question using data from the graphs below. *How does the amount of carbon dioxide in the atmosphere relate to temperature?*

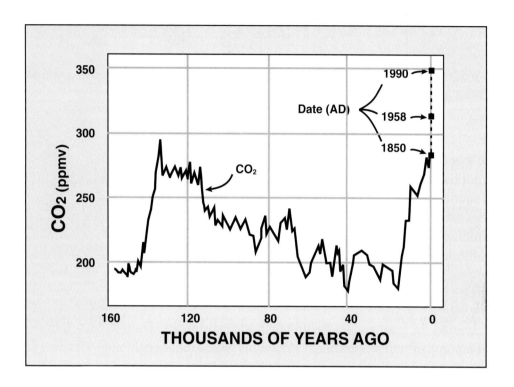

**Figure : Changes in Carbon Dioxide Levels for the Past 160,000 Years
(Derived from Ice Core Data, US Global Change Research Program.)**

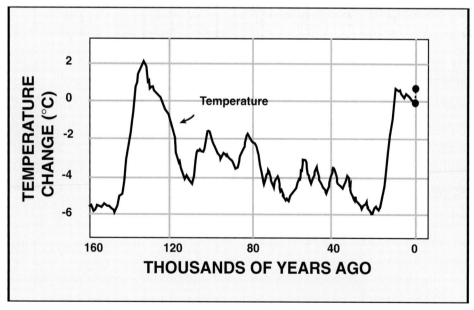

**Figure : Changes in Temperature for the Past 160,000 Years
(Derived from Ice Core Data, US Global Change Research Program.)**

Global Carbon Cycle

? *Essential Question: How does carbon dioxide enter and leave the atmosphere?*

Overview

You have learned that carbon dioxide levels in the atmosphere have increased over the past 100 years. How could this happen, especially if plants take up carbon dioxide during photosynthesis? All we have to do is plant more trees and the problem would be solved, right?

Time is the reason we can't just plant more trees to solve the problem. Trees take time to mature and turn carbon from CO_2 into sugars. Also, when trees die, some of the carbon is re-introduced into the atmosphere. To think about solutions to the problem, we must first understand the time it takes carbon to move through its natural cycle. How long does it take for carbon to move from one "reservoir" to the next? In this activity, you will create a concept map of the carbon cycle.

Materials

a web browser

Carbon Website
File name: **index.htm**
File type: HTML file

Procedure

1. A reservoir is a place where carbon (in the form of coal, carbon dioxide, living tissue, or other compounds) can collect. As you go through the presentation, write down the name of each major <u>carbon reservoir</u> on an index card.

2. A flux is a movement of carbon from one place to another. When you find a <u>flux</u>, draw an arrow on an index card. Label it with the flux name and amount.

3. When you are finished, place the cards on a table. Arrange them in such a way that the right flux arrows connect the reservoirs.

Analysis Questions

1. Draw a picture of the global carbon cycle. Label all reservoirs and fluxes in your diagram.

2. Look at all the fluxes into and out of the atmosphere. Complete the Carbon Flux table below, then answer this question:

   Based on the total flux into and out of the atmosphere, is the atmosphere reservoir gaining or losing carbon? What might be the reason for this?

3. Compare the different fluxes in your drawing. The fluxes represent pathways for the carbon to move from one reservoir to the next. Remember: the fluxes are in grams of carbon per year. Which flux provides the slowest pathway for carbon to be removed from the atmosphere?

4. Based on the reservoirs in the carbon cycle diagram, where is most carbon stored?

5. How long would it take for all the carbon stored as "recoverable fossil fuel" to be consumed by burning fossil fuels?

6. Answer the essential question: *How does carbon dioxide enter and leave the atmosphere?*

Carbon Flux

Into the Atmosphere		Out of the Atmosphere	
From	**Flux (10^{15} g C/yr)**	**Into**	**Flux (10^{15} g C/yr)**
Cold ocean surface		Cold ocean surface	
Warm ocean surface		Warm ocean surface	
Soil and detritus		Biota (plants)	
Biota (animals)			
Fossil fuel			
emissions			
Deforestation (purposely burning trees)			
Total:		Total:	

Human Activities

? ***Essential Question:*** *What are some steps you can take personally to reduce the greenhouse gases in the atmosphere?*

Procedure

In our modern lives, each of us contributes some carbon dioxide to the atmosphere. Thus, we all add to the problem of global climate change. There are changes you can make in your life to limit your part in climate change. Read the following article. Answer the analysis questions.

Where do greenhouse gases come from?

The human connection

Many important human activities emit greenhouse gases. Emissions started to rise sharply in the 1800s when the Industrial Revolution began. Industries at the time ran mostly on coal. Also, urban centers grew very quickly. Land once covered with forests and fields was sacrificed to industrial development.

Today, industry is even more widespread and very dependent on electricity. Most of the electricity is generated by coal-burning power plants. Nearly every aspect of our lives involves the consumption of electricity. Populations in most developed countries, especially the United States, rely on cars for transportation and trucks for the transport of goods. In developing countries, increasing populations are using more automobiles. They are becoming an essential part of modern life. The fossil fuels and greenhouse gases they produce are becoming an important part of the global economy.

People Burn Fossil Fuels

The largest source of greenhouse gas emissions from human activities is the burning of fossil fuels. The use of fossil fuels accounts for about three-quarters of mankind's carbon dioxide (CO_2) emissions. Billions of tons of carbon are released into the atmosphere every year. Human activity produces one-fifth of the methane (CH_4) and much of the nitrous oxide (N_2O) that is emitted every year. Human activities also release nitrogen oxides (NOx), hydrocarbons (HCs), and carbon monoxide (CO). These are not greenhouse gases, but they can influence the presence of greenhouse gases in the atmosphere.

The combustion of oil, natural gas, and coal provides most of the energy we use every day. The energy is used to produce electricity, run automobiles, heat houses, and power factories. If these fuels burned completely, the only carbon-based by-product of their combustion would be carbon dioxide. However, combustion is often incomplete, so carbon monoxide (CO), sulfur oxides, and hydrocarbons are also produced.

People Process Fossil Fuels

Sometimes, the release of greenhouse gases is deliberate. When natural gas is vented from oil wells, it emits carbon dioxide and methane. The release of greenhouse gases also results from accidents or leaks, especially in the oil industry. Methane, which occurs naturally in coal, is released when coal is mined. (Sometimes, this methane is collected and used as a natural gas.). Hydrocarbons can enter the atmosphere in several ways. Oil spills from ships and small losses during the fueling of motor vehicles release hydrocarbons. When plastic trash is burned, hydrocarbons enter the atmosphere because they are a key component of plastics.

People Cutting Down or Burning of Forests

Deforestation is the second largest source of carbon dioxide in the air. When forests are cleared for farming or development, the trees are burned. Most of the carbon in the burned or decomposing trees escapes to the atmosphere. However, when new forests are planted, the growing trees absorb carbon dioxide, removing it from the atmosphere. In the tropics, more forests are being cleared and burned than are being planted. Thus, there is a net loss of carbon in the forest and a net gain of carbon released to the air. There is much scientific uncertainty about emissions from deforestation. Estimates range from 600 million to 2.6 billion metric tons of carbon being released every year from this source.

There is still some uncertainty about the role of trees in absorbing carbon dioxide from the atmosphere. During photosynthesis, trees and plants remove carbon dioxide from the air. The soil also absorbs and holds carbon compounds for a thousand years or more. For years, scientists developed computer models in which forests and soil were thought to moderate global warming. Scientists have recently discovered, however, that trees have a limit to how much carbon dioxide they can absorb. Once they reach their "maximum" amount, they begin giving off carbon dioxide into the atmosphere. This is already happening in the Amazon rainforest. Trees there are so saturated with carbon dioxide, they are now emitting the gas. Recent studies also show that farming causes soil to give up some of the carbon it stores. As the human population continues to grow, more and more land is plowed up. So, soil will contribute more and more carbon in the atmosphere. Clearly, trees and soil can no longer be treated solely as carbon absorbers. New computer models will have to reflect these discoveries to be accurate in predicting global warming.

People Making Cement

Cement production accounts for 2.5% of CO_2 emissions from industrial sources. As with fossil fuels, the carbon dioxide released during cement production comes from fossils. It comes from limestone ($CaCO_3$), which is mostly sea shells and other biomass buried in ancient ocean sediments.

People Keeping Domesticated Animals

The third most important greenhouse gas, after water vapor and carbon dioxide, is methane. Domesticated animals emit methane as a by-product of digestion when they belch. Methane is produced by cattle, dairy cows, goats, sheep, camels, pigs, and horses. The methane emissions are produced by the fermentation of food by microbes in the animals' digestive tracts. Methane is also produced by the decomposition of animal manure. Methane emissions from human's livestock activities total about 100 million metric tons a year. As you can see, methane occurs at far lower concentrations in the atmosphere than carbon dioxide. However, it is a much more powerful greenhouse gas because it absorbs some solar radiation that other greenhouse gases do not.

People Cultivating Rice

Rice cultivation also releases methane. Wetland rice farming produces about one-fifth of global methane emissions from human activities. Wetland rice is grown in fields that are flooded or irrigated for much of the growing season. Bacteria and other microorganisms in the flooded soil decompose organic matter and produce methane.

People Produce and Dispose of Lots of Garbage

The disposal and treatment of trash and human waste also produces methane. When garbage is buried in a landfill, it eventually decomposes and emits methane and some carbon dioxide. Unless the gas is captured and used as a fuel, the methane eventually escapes to the atmosphere. This source of methane is more common near cities which have central landfills. In rural areas, garbage is usually left to decompose in the open air. Methane is also emitted when human waste is treated in sewage plants.

People Using Fertilizer

Fertilizer use on crops increases nitrous oxide emissions. The nitrogen contained in many fertilizers aids the natural processes carried out by bacteria and other microbes in the soil. These processes convert some nitrogen into nitrous oxide. The amount of N_2O emitted depends on the type and amount of fertilizer, soil conditions, and climate. This complex relationship is not yet fully understood.

People Keeping Cool: Chlorofluorocarbons

Industry creates chlorofluorocarbons (CFCs) for use in various products and industrial processes. They are used particularly in refrigeration and air conditioning. CFCs have been released in large quantities into the atmosphere since the 1950s. They have been used in aerosol cans, in the manufacture of plastics, in the cooling coils of refrigerators and air conditioners, in fire extinguishers, and as solvents for cleaning. Scientists eventually discovered that CFCs were responsible for damage to Earth's ozone layer. In 1987, the manufacture and use of CFCs was banned. Since then, atmospheric concentrations of CFCs have nearly stabilized and are expected to continue to decline. CFC substitutes, such as HCFCs, (CFCs with hydrogen atoms added) cause less damage to the ozone layer, but are still potent greenhouse gases.

Analysis Questions

1. Planting more trees might not be the answer to removing carbon dioxide from the atmosphere. Why not?

2. Which of the activities described above do you think occur more often in developed countries rather than in developing countries?

3. Which of the described activities do you take part in or are connected to your life in some way?

4. Which of the activities do you think could be most easily changed to reduce their greenhouse gas emissions? Why?

5. Answer the essential question: *What are some steps you can take personally to reduce the greenhouse gases in the atmosphere?*

Human Population and Carbon Dioxide

Essential Question: *Which country has the highest CO$_2$ emissions per capita?*

Materials

Computers running WorldWatcher

Datasets:

> **Carbon Emissions 1987.wwf**
>
> **Population Density 1984.wwf**

Procedure

1. Open the dataset **Carbon Emissions 1987.wwf** in WorldWatcher. In your notebook, describe the units of carbon emission used in this dataset.

2. Record the three areas of the world that emit the most carbon from burning fossil fuels.

3. Record the three areas of the world that emit the least carbon.

4. Open the dataset **Population Density 1984.wwf**.

5. Use the window math operator. Create a visualization that shows carbon emissions per person per year.

> ### Stop and Think
>
> What does this new visualization tell you about the relationship between carbon dioxide emissions and population density?

6. Record the location with the highest carbon dioxide emission per person per year.

Analysis Questions

1. Of the three areas with the highest emissions, which contain the most developed countries? Which of the three lowest emitting areas contain the most developing countries?

2. Answer the essential question: *Which country has the highest CO$_2$ emissions per capita?*

Lesson 7
Misconceptions

 Driving Question: *Much of what we hear in the news about climate change is misleading. How can it be presented accurately?*

Overview

In this chapter, you have explored the science of climate as it relates to temperature on Earth. You have studied how the Sun's energy heats the Earth. You have studied how the greenhouse effect increases the temperature at the Earth's surface. You have also studied how carbon dioxide and other gases contribute to the greenhouse effect, possibly causing climate change. The greenhouse effect could have serious consequences for Earth's climate. It could have a negative impact on growing seasons, polar ice caps, sea level, as well as other unpredictable consequences. Unfortunately, many people have wrong information about climate change. This often prevents them from making sound decisions about energy use.

In this lesson, you will apply what you have learned to respond to citizens who misunderstand the issue. In this chapter, you will explore alternative energy sources. These energy sources could alleviate some of the stress put on our atmosphere by carbon dioxide emissions.

Important Content

- Arguments used to support claims about global climate change are still being debated, and the data to support those claims is inconclusive.

- If climate change occurs, the possible effects could include: volatile weather systems, melting ice caps, rising sea levels, and ecosystem changes.

Letters

Essential Question: *What are the common misconceptions about global climate change?*

Overview

You are a science advisor to Congressman Mark Clybourn. It is your job to address the issues raised by his constituents who are concerned about global climate change. Below are three letters from citizens requesting that Congressman Clybourn take some course of action. Compose a reply to each letter, responding to the concerns of each citizen. Unfortunately, not all of the citizens are as informed about the facts of climate change as you are. You may need to correct their mistakes. Be sure to back up your answers with evidence so that no one can accuse you of providing incorrect information!

Procedure

Your teacher will assign you one letter to answer with a reply. Be sure to include evidence to support any statements you make.

Then answer the essential question: *What are some common misconceptions about global climate change?*

Letter 1

Congressman Mark Clybourn
1 Leadership Way
Washington, D.C. 06182

Dear Congressman Clybourn,

I am writing to you to demand that something be done about global warming. This most recent spat of serious warming is killing all the azaleas in my garden! As a resident of this area all my life, I can tell you that I have never seen hot weather like this before. Fifteen straight days of temperatures over 95 degrees. That is just unbearable! Why, just yesterday it was nearly hot enough to fry an egg on the sidewalk!

In all my years I've seen plenty of summers, but this summer has been something else. Would you believe that I have been forced to resort to using the neighborhood kid's Slip n' Slide thing for a little relief?!? At the rate things are heating up around here, it's likely to be so hot in December that I'll never see a white Christmas again.

As a member of the United States government, it is your sworn duty to protect me, my tulips, and my rhododendrons (along with the rest of the country I suppose) from the runaway effects of global warming. I insist that you take action to alter the course of this climate change immediately!

Sincerely,

Ms. Ima Greenthumb

Ms. Ima Greenthumb
Concerned Citizen

Letter 2

Congressman Mark Clybourn
1 Leadership Way
Washington, D.C. 06182

Dear Congressman Clybourn,

I am writing to request your help in finding government funding to pay for the further development of my latest invention, a device that I feel will be of enormous benefit to our whole society.

As a member of the scientific community, I feel it is my duty to impress upon you the need to deal with the greenhouse effect problem. Most notably, the greenhouse effect is causing the entire planet to heat up and is raising the average temperature around the world. The greenhouse effect will undoubtedly continue affecting our planet until greenhouse gases are eliminated. Luckily, the greenhouse effect does not need to be a nuisance to us or to our planet Earth any longer. I have a solution!

My invention, the Greenhouse Gas Guzzler, GGG for short, has the potential to rid the planet of all greenhouse gases. While I cannot reveal to you the inner workings of the GGG, (I have a patent pending), I can tell you that in laboratory tests, the GGG has successfully collected and destroyed each and every greenhouse gas in its immediate vicinity. Just think, life in the future without any greenhouse gases. Our greenhouse effect problems would be solved.

As the greenhouse effect impacts the lives of each and every one of your constituents, I am sure you feel as strongly as I do about this important issue. Unfortunately, with the limited private funding I have had so far, I have only been able to develop a miniature GGG device, which is capable of removing the greenhouse gases from a volume of air about the size of a breadbox. As you can imagine, I will need many hundreds of millions of dollars to build a GGG device large enough to rid the entire planet of greenhouse gases. If you will support my research with federal funding, I assure you I will be able to rid the world of greenhouse gases forever.

Sincerely,

Dr. I. Cicle , Ph.D.

Dr. I. Cicle , Ph.D.
Chief Scientist, Project 3G

Letter 3

Congressman Mark Clybourn
1 Leadership Way
Washington, D.C. 06182

Dear Congressman Clybourn,

I am writing to you because I would like the Environmental Protection Agency (EPA) to reconsider their decision to reject Widget Inc.'s request for approval to build a new widget factory, on the grounds that the factory would produce too much carbon dioxide. As Widget Inc.'s CEO, I know that our history of burning fossil fuels in our factories has been something of a blemish on the company's reputation. I would, however, like to reassure you that we at Widget Inc. are taking the environment very seriously.

Our company's research has shown that burning fossil fuels is an essential part of Widget production. Although burning fossil fuels releases large amounts of carbon dioxide into the atmosphere, we at Widget Inc. believe we have found an acceptable solution that will bring the total emissions from our site down to an acceptable level.

We propose planting 100 acres of forest surrounding our new factory, thus quickly and completely absorbing ALL of the carbon dioxide produced by the factory. By planting all these trees, the factory would have no adverse impact on the environment!

I honestly cannot understand how the EPA could have a problem with Widget Inc.'s emissions, considering how the carbon dioxide we produce will be immediately absorbed by all the trees we plant. As a citizen who contributes large amounts of money to your election campaign, I implore you to exercise your influence with the EPA and to act on our behalf.

Sincerely,

Mr. Smoky Stack, M.B.A.

Mr. Smoky Stack, M.B.A.

CEO, Widget Inc.

Alternative Energy

Chapter 6
Alternative Energy

Connections

For many years, scientists have been looking for good alternatives to fossil fuels to generate electricity. In previous chapters, you reviewed the environmental problems that can arise from using fossil fuels. One of the most serious problems with fossil fuel combustion is global climate change. Human behavior is affecting the world's climate. This is why we need to focus on alternative ways to generate energy that do not produce as much greenhouse gas. As the human population grows, its demand for electricity and other types of energy increases.

This chapter presents a task similar to the one in Chapter 4. This time, however, you will not be restricted to using a coal-burning power plant. You will again be selecting a location for a power plant based on the resources available to a region. Many of the issues you will address will be similar to those in Chapter 4. You will explore land use, social and political considerations, and the power plant's impact on the environment.

In this chapter:

You have learned that fossil-fuel burning power plants help create acid rain, smog, and global warming. This chapter begins by introducing you to alternative energy sources. These alternative energies offer a solution to the problems caused by fossil fuels. However, you will discover that the alternatives are not perfect either. Each has benefits and drawbacks, both positive and negative environmental impacts. Once you are familiar with the alternative energy sources, you will complete the final project for the unit. For a specific geographic location, you will use data in ArcView to assess available resources. Your task will be to balance the location's available resources with the benefits of alternative energy sources. You will then decide on one alternative source of energy to generate power. At the end of the chapter, you will present your final decision to the class.

When you're done you'll be able to:

*   compare the benefits and drawbacks of different energy generation options.

*   assess available resources to determine if a site is appropriate for a power plant.

*   analyze decisions about energy that could affect global climate change.

Lesson 1
What Are the Alternatives?

Driving Question: What options do we have to replace fossil fuels?

Overview

This lesson focuses on alternative energy sources. You will split into groups and do research on one alternative energy source. You will complete a report that includes how your alternative energy power plant works, the benefits of using that energy source, and the environmental impacts of using that type of power. You will present your research results to your classmates and they will use your information in later decisions. It is important that the information you share with them is accurate and complete.

Important Content

- Sources of electricity other than fossil fuels are available, but not as widely used. These include hydroelectric power, solar power, power from biomass, nuclear power, and others.

- There are many different energy transformations that might lead to useful power generation.

- Alternative power plants use many of the same principles as fossil-fuel power plants in the generation of electricity: only the energy source is different.

What Are the Alternatives to Fossil Fuels?

Essential Questions: *What do you think is the best alternative to fossil fuels? Why?*

Overview

You have seen that many human activities involve the combustion of fossil fuels. These activities emit carbon dioxide and other greenhouse gases, which cause global warming. Electricity production in the United States often involves the combustion of coal. Coal combustion emits huge amounts of carbon dioxide into the air. About 1.5 million metric tons of carbon dioxide is released every year from coal combustion. Coal is also a non-renewable resource. We will eventually run out of coal and other fossil fuels.

Huge amounts of energy are used every day. Energy is needed to heat and cool buildings. It is needed to provide light to your classroom and home. It is needed to transport people and goods. There is a great need for new forms of energy to power modern life. This has led scientists to develop technology that uses alternative energy sources.

Analysis Questions

1. As a class, make a list of alternatives to coal that could provide energy for humans. Does your community, or other communities you may know about, produce electricity using alternative energy technology? What energy source do they use?

2. Look at the list your class has put together. What are some of the advantages and disadvantages of each alternative way of producing electricity?

3. Answer the essential questions: *What do you think is the best alternative to fossil fuels? Why?*

Research

Essential Questions: *What other sources of energy can generate electricity?*
How do they work?

Overview

Your job in this activity is to become an expert on one alternative energy source to use in a power plant. You will share your knowledge with your classmates in a few days when you give an oral report on your findings. As you gather information, be aware of where it is coming from and any biases or inaccuracies you might find. Your report should include how electricity is generated using this type of alternative energy. It should also include how this type of power generation might affect the environment.

Procedure

Your teacher will provide your group with an alternative energy source to research. Prepare a written report according to the guidelines below. In the process, remember to keep an eye out for biased information. Some of the groups you encounter during your research may be advancing their own opinions. They might present biased information to support only their own views.

Sections of Your Report

- Draw a diagram of the alternative energy power plant layout. Label all the parts.

- Write a description of how the power plant generates electricity.

- Draw an input/output diagram of the power plant. Remember to fill in mass and energy sources.

- Describe the benefits of using this type of power. Describe the problems in using this type of power.

- Create a bibliography of books, articles, web sites, and other information sources you used to obtain your information.

- Your report should also include information to complete the chart in Lesson 1: *Alternative Energy Summary*.

Five Alternatives

Procedure

Read the section below that refers to your assigned alternative energy source. This background information will help you get your research started.

Wind Energy

Wind is a force of nature that is renewable. The use of wind energy is not new. People have used windmills to do work for them for hundreds of years. Today's scientists have developed highly efficient windmills to take the energy in the wind and convert it into electrical energy. The wind forces the windmill's blades, called propellers, to turn. This rotation turns a shaft that forces a turbine to produce electricity. 'Wind farms' are areas populated with many wind turbines, where the wind blows strongly throughout the year. However, a problem with wind energy is that very little of it can be stored. This means energy generation stops when the wind is not blowing. Another limit on wind energy is that the wind is not always blowing strongly. This means in large-scale power generation, wind power is only used as a supplement to other energy sources. From 1880 to 1930, the U.S.'s rural areas were not electrified. During this time, over 6 million windmills generated electric power in rural areas of the western U.S.

Environmental impacts of wind farms are few. They include noise pollution and the risk that birds might fly near and get caught in the rotating blades of a windmill. Also, large areas of land must be set aside for wind turbines to produce large amounts of electric power, interfering with other land uses. However, there is one advantage of wind farms. Since the turbines are high in the air, their bases occupy only about 5% of the land. That leaves the bulk of the land available for agriculture, grazing, or other uses. Increasingly, wind farms are sited on platforms in the ocean, where they do not interfere with land-use practices. The wind conditions are also less gusty on the ocean, allowing for more constant electricity generation.

Solar Energy

Plants have used solar energy since the beginning of time through photosynthesis. The Sun's energy has heated the Earth's surface and created its weather patterns since the Earth first formed. Scientists and engineers have now developed many technologies to harness the Sun's energy. We will focus on the use of solar energy to produce electricity.

The amount of sunlight is unlimited and free, making it a renewable energy source. Energy from the Sun can be converted into electricity using solar cells (called photovoltaic, or PV cells). These silicon crystal cells are very small. A few put together may be as small as 2 square centimeters in area, as in hand-held calculators. Or, many of them may work together in larger structures called "solar panels." Panels range in size from a few square feet in area to many square meters. Larger solar panels power orbiting satellites or single-family homes. Many solar panels may be linked together in one large system to generate more electricity. Powering an entire city with solar energy would require a large amount of space that may not be easy to find. Building tops, however, provide a practical location for solar panels. Solar panels must be located in areas with lots of Sun. The solar collectors only convert sunlight to energy when the Sun is shining. Again, the storage of solar energy is limited. Batteries can only store solar energy for a few hours. This makes solar energy a good supplemental energy source but not a primary energy source.

There are some other drawbacks to solar energy. The structures required for collecting, storing and converting solar energy into electricity are often expensive. Solar cells also create some hazardous wastes that need to be properly contained. Solar panels are easily damaged by hail, wind, and ultraviolet radiation. Still, scientists are developing solar panels that are increasingly more durable and efficient.

Energy from Biomass (organic matter)

Energy from biomass is one of the most common forms of fuel used in the world today. If you have a fireplace at home, you are using biomass as an energy source. (Trees are organic matter.) Biomass is the production of power by burning vegetation matter like trees, paper, lumberyard or agricultural waste, etc. It also includes burning animal and municipal waste. There is a biomass power plant in southern California that burns 40 tons of cow manure every hour. This plant generates enough electricity for 20,000 homes.

There are different technologies for converting biomass to electricity. The best technologies for biomass power plants are similar to power plants that burn coal, oil, and natural gas. However, biomass plants are less efficient. Biomass fuels are burned in a boiler to produce heat. Heat exchangers are used to convert water to steam. The steam drives a turbine connected to a generator that produces electricity. Technology is under development to convert biomass into gas. These plants are expected to have higher efficiency and fewer emissions.

As with every form of alternative energy, using biomass involves tradeoffs. Where excess farmland is available, local farmers can sustain growth of fast-growing trees and grasses. This creates jobs and stimulates the local economy, but the cost of the fuel is higher than coal. Crop and forest residues can be collected at a lower cost, but some must be left on the ground to replenish the soil with nutrients. Clearcutting forests for energy has been used in the past. However, whole ecosystems are destroyed this way and nutrient recycling is disrupted. If people burn trash, they are reducing the amount of organic material that ends up in landfills. However, unless the trash has been well separated to eliminate contamination, it increases air pollution.

Hydroelectric Energy

Hydroelectric power uses the energy in flowing water to produce power. The water spins a turbine connected to a generator that produces electricity. Hydropower is most effective in locations with large changes in elevation that produce fast river flows. The water may come from rivers, streams, or lakes. Hydropower is a cheap, clean, and reliable way to produce electricity. It currently produces a significant fraction of the electricity used in the U.S., (particularly in the Pacific Northwest) and around the world. To use hydropower, construction of a dam is usually necessary. However, the building of a hydroelectric system alters its natural surroundings. The flow of rivers is altered, river valleys are flooded, habitats are destroyed for many fish, and people lose their homes and have to be relocated. Fish like salmon that need to swim up and down river as part of their reproductive life-cycle are especially affected by these projects. Many people are concerned about the environmental effects of blocking streams, rivers, or lakes to create dams. Effects on the environment must be considered carefully during a hydroelectric project to avoid damage to ecosystems. Hydroelectric plants can also have a positive effect on the environment. The dams often produce a body of water that benefits different species, like still-water fish and waterfowl. Hydropower is not always considered renewable because dams have a limited "life span." Eventually, a build-up of sediment makes the dams inoperable. Old, unusable dams become a safety hazard to people and animals. Many of the best rivers for hydropower in the U.S. have already been dammed.

Nuclear Energy

Nuclear energy is the energy that exists within the nucleus of an atom. Powerful forces bind together the parts of the atomic nucleus. Nuclear fission is the nuclear power used today. Fission breaks the bonds holding the parts of the nucleus together, releasing huge amounts of energy. Fission is also used in atomic bombs, where the breakup of atomic nuclei creates a chain reaction and an atomic explosion. In a nuclear power plant, this process is controlled and slowed down. The energy from this process delivers heat, which is used to boil water. Once again, this produces steam to drive a steam turbine connected to a generator that produces electricity.

The most commonly used nuclear material is uranium. Nuclear power is so efficient that one (1) gram of uranium-235 delivers about as much energy as 3,500,000 grams of coal. Well-designed nuclear power plants can run for years without having to be refueled or shut down. Nuclear energy has one enormous advantage – it does not produce gases such as CO_2.

There are many drawbacks to nuclear power, however. Nuclear power plants are elaborate and expensive to build. They create radioactive waste that has to be contained for thousands of years. Some of today's nuclear power plants store this waste on site. Nuclear material in large concentrations is very harmful to humans, plants and animals. There is currently a heated controversy in the U.S. about where to create safe, long-term storage for nuclear waste. The storage site must safely contain the waste for thousands of years. Nuclear plants also produce large amounts of water vapor by cooling hot water byproducts. Water vapor is a greenhouse gas and a pollutant. Another disadvantage of nuclear power is that nuclear fuel (uranium) is in short supply. At current yearly consumption by power plants and weapons facilities, there's about a 200-300-year supply left.

The worst aspect of nuclear power is the danger of accidents if the power plant is not properly maintained. The former Soviet Union had one of the worst nuclear disasters ever. In 1986, a test was run at the Chernobyl nuclear power plant, near Kiev, without following proper procedures. The result was a core explosion that destroyed one of the power plant reactors. Poisonous radioactive steam and smoke were emitted into the atmosphere. The government dumped 5000 tons of boron, sand, clay, and lead on the site to try to stop the burning and limit the release of radioactive particles. The core burned for nine days. Thirty people died in the explosion and there were 134 cases of fatal radiation poisoning. Birth defects and abnormally high numbers of childhood leukemia are still being seen in the area because of the disaster. The total number of affected people numbers in the thousands. The site around the reactor will remain uninhabitable indefinitely.

Hybrid Energy

A major problem with wind, solar, and hydropower is an inconsistent power level. However, wind, solar, hydroelectric, and biomass power can be combined into a single reliable energy source. It also has relatively minimal pollution compared to fossil or nuclear fuel sources. These systems are called hybrid and rely on the strengths of each of the alternative energy sources. For example, surplus solar energy can be used to pump water uphill that can be drained at night to produce hydropower. It is often windier at night or during storms. Therefore, wind power can provide energy when solar power is weak. These energy sources, combined with renewable biomass burning can produce a more constant power supply.

The main drawback with hybrid power is the need for multiple systems to function together. This increases the number of problems to manage. It seems unlikely, that even hybrid power can work well enough on its own in the near future. The alternatives are helpful but there is still a need for fossil fuel or nuclear power as a supplement. However, to minimize human impact on the environment, the use of multiple energy sources seems better than relying on a dwindling fossil fuel supply. Also, developing renewable and hybrid technologies will reduce the future environmental and economic stresses of a dwindling energy supply.

Alternative Energy Summary

As you gather information for your alternative energy presentation, make sure you include all the information needed to complete this chart. Fill in the information in the chart as you find it. As you listen to your classmates' reports, take notes to gather this essential information about each energy source.

Basic Information on Alternative Energy Sources

Power Plant Type	Primary Energy Source	Geographic Distribution and Abundance of Resource	Is it moveable?	Local Resources Needed	Major Waste and Pollutants (Environmental Impacts)			Other impacts	Cost of building and maintaining
					Solid	Gas	Liquid		
Fossil Fuel (Coal, Natural Gas)	Coal or Natural Gas	Found all over the world; in the United States, found primarily in the Appalachians and in the Western States of Wyoming and the Dakotas	Yes, by train or road (train is cheaper)	Water	Mercury (poisons fish and consumers), ash	Carbon dioxide, ozone, nitrogen oxides cause smog, sulfur dioxide causes acid rain, carbon monoxide causes asthma, methane contributes to global warming	Thermal (adds heat to lake water that kills fish and other animals)	Mining coal can pollute water supplies and alter the landscape.	Relatively cheap, 4-5 cents per Megawatt
Wind									
Biomass									
Hydro-electric									
Solar									
Nuclear									

Lesson 2

Setting the Stage

Driving Question: *What are the constraints and considerations on this decision?*

Overview

You now know the basics about different types of alternative energy sources. This lesson will introduce you to a situation where you can apply that knowledge. Three locations in the U.S. are searching for alternative energy sources. Your task will be to help these communities find a balanced solution to their energy problems. You will learn about these three locations in the next several lessons. You will consider their populations and social situations. You will use the environmental decision making process to keep track of the consequences of your possible decision.

Important Content

- When determining the best way to generate electricity for a community, it is important to look at the available local resources.

Letter from NEPC

Overview

It is time to apply the information you have about alternative energy sources to a real problem. In this lesson, you are part of a team of environmental scientists. Your specialty is planning and implementing alternative energy resources. The letter in this activity outlines your tasks and goals.

Procedure

Read the letter and answer the questions below. Be prepared to share your results with the group.

Analysis Questions

1. In your own words, describe what you're being asked to do.

2. Develop a brief outline of your project report.

3. What additional information will you need to complete your project?

National Energy Planning Commission
123 Main Boulevard, Washington, DC

Dear Energy Researcher,

The Municipal Power Boards of the areas surrounding Burlington, Vermont; Laramie, Wyoming; and Albuquerque, New Mexico have asked for our assistance in selecting an appropriate alternative energy for their cities. These cities are growing rapidly and need more power. Thankfully, by contacting us, they show concern for a clean environment and an investment in the future of energy. With your direction, a new power plant will be added to each city's existing grid. Consumers from these cities have agreed to pay more for electricity, since they know it will not be coming from fossil fuels.

In order for the project to provide enough power to make a difference in reducing the overall pollution in each area, each power plant needs to generate at least 100 megawatts (MW) of power. The local politicians are also concerned about keeping costs as low as possible and providing local jobs. Therefore, each power plant should be within the study area defined by each county power board. Each power plant should make use of the resources available in the local area.

Together with a team of fellow researchers, you will devise a proposal for one area's new alternative power source. Your proposal should contain a list of the best three alternative power plants for that area, describing for each the type and specific location. You'll need to provide the evidence that informed your decision and the methods and techniques you used in the decision-making process.

Your team will present your proposal to the county power board, which will make the final decision. The board is made up of local citizens who are interested in providing clean, reliable, and safe power to their community. Please note that they do not have any specialized knowledge of power plants, so your proposal must explain in clear language why yours is the best option for their community. You must also assist them as much as possible in making the final decision.

Sincerely,

Richard H. Truly
Director

Location Background

Essential Question: *What social or political factors should you keep in mind while making your decision?*

Overview

Deciding what type of power to use can be a social and political decision. If a local river is a favorite spot for fishermen, they will not support a plan to build a dam and a hydroelectric plant there. If people are worried about sulfur dioxide emissions from a local chemical factory, they may not accept a new power plant that will add to that problem. It is important to learn about the people who live in the area where you are building the power plant. It helps you to predict what their reactions might be to alternative ways of generating power.

Procedure

Read the description of your location. Think about what it might mean when you are choosing a power plant.

Analysis Questions

1. What is the population of the largest city in your study area?

2. What is the major industry or source of revenue for the city and the region?

3. List two things that make the location an attractive place to live. What specific negative impacts do you want to avoid?

4. Answer the essential question: *What social or political factors should you keep in mind while making your decision?*

Albuquerque, New Mexico

In Albuquerque, New Mexico (pop. 385,000), you will find a combination of Native American, Mexican, rural, and urban cultures. The city has a beautiful backdrop of big sky, mountains, and mesas.

Albuquerque is a city with a long history of ethnic diversity. The Anasazi and Pueblo Indians inhabited the city in the years 1000-1500. The Spanish conquistadors arrived next and later Europeans, Asians, and African Americans. Within the last few decades, Mexican immigration has heavily influenced the city of Albuquerque.

Abuelita is a small neighborhood in Albuquerque. It has been described as "one of those New Mexican medleys of culture and race, where moccasins walk next to cowboy boots in the aisles of the old-time grocery, and Spanish, Keresan, and English mix easily at the Pizza Hut buffet."

The city of Albuquerque is growing bigger and becoming more urban. City officials say that Albuquerque is on the verge of great transformations. It is predicted that by 2050, concern will grow for small school districts, rural areas, mining, gas, oil, and agriculture. Citizens will refocus attention to the problems of overcrowding and its impact on the environment. Issues such as air pollution, transportation, and water shortages will take center stage.

Tourism is one of Albuquerque's largest sources of income. In 1999, the city raised over $8.4 million in lodging taxes alone. People come from all over to see the Sandia Mountains, the Rio Grande rift, the volcanoes of the West Mesa, the Ciabola National forest, ice caves, and other natural wonders. For the beauty of its colorful landscape, New Mexico is known as the Land of Enchantment. In Albuquerque, one can take the nation's longest aerial tramway to the top of Sandia Peak and, in the winter, ski or snowboard. There are also annual festivals, including the world's largest hot-air balloon festival, hang gliding festivals, and several bird watching festivals. The city is unique because it has four seasons, four life zones, and three distinct geologic regions. Often, enchanted tourists become residents. Travelers often arrive in Albuquerque via the famous Route 66 highway. As evidence of the state's beauty, New

Mexico's portion of the road was designated a national scenic highway by the Federal Highway Administration in 2000.

Burlington, Vermont

If you were to walk along the streets of downtown Burlington, Vermont, you would see successful, privately owned stores next to major corporate retail outlets. You would come across Burlington's famous Ben and Jerry's ice cream parlors. On the shores of Lake Champlain, you would see families renting boats and bikers pedaling along a nine-mile-long bike path. You would see a city that has been molded by its open-minded people, progressive politics, and environmental concerns.

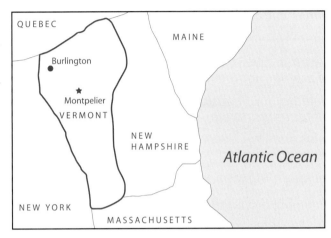

Burlington, Vermont (pop. 40,259) is a town made up of liberal, environmentally friendly, family-oriented people who all share a deep affinity for their city. The city prides itself on having one of the lowest crime and unemployment rates in the nation. Its constituents average about $50,800 in annual family income. Most people live and work in suburbs. The downtown area is reserved for shopping, dining, and entertainment. It is also a city where diversity thrives. For instance, the old north end is home to French Canadians, Irish Catholics, African Americans, Vietnamese, and Latinos, who care greatly about their community and its youth. Art festivals, performances, and educational opportunities are offered in abundance. The University of Vermont is located in Burlington.

Burlington's political views are quite different from those of most of the rest of the nation. Burlington citizens have strayed from the two-party system. More than ten years ago, Burlington elected Bernie Sanders, an Independent, as mayor of the city. During his tenure, he made Burlington one of the first towns in the country to give equal rights to domestic partners. He also reversed the increasing gap between rich and poor. Now a congressman, Sanders struggles to apply Burlington's successes to the rest of the nation. As one of the only Independents in Congress, Sanders proposed an economic policy, "so that, for a change, the economy booms for the middle class and working class, rather than for millionaires and billionaires."

The greatest source of pollution in Burlington comes from automobiles. One concerted effort to solve this problem has resulted in a $3-million investment in public transit.

Burlington has also taken admirable steps toward cleaning up Lake Champlain. Well above the national average, 40% of Burlington's solid waste is recycled.

Laramie, Wyoming

Laramie, Wyoming (pop. 27,000) lies between the Laramie Mountains and the Medicine Bow Mountains in southern Wyoming. It is known for its beautiful scenery and fresh air. It has an average summer high of 80 degrees and an average winter high of 40 degrees.

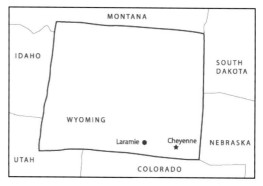

In 1999, *Outdoor Magazine* named Laramie "the best place to raise an outdoor family." It's no wonder. Laramie is surrounded by several hundred thousand acres of public land, including national forests, state and national parks, and wilderness areas. People who enjoy skiing, mountain climbing, camping, fishing, and hunting, affectionately refer to it as "the gem in the mountains."

Laramie was established in 1868 after the Union Pacific Railroad decided to make the area its last stop on the western train route. Named after a local fur trader, Laramie was a model of a western town. Today the western influences, along with the historic buildings, still remain. What's different is the new flavor the University of Wyoming has given to the town. The University of Wyoming is the only four-year college in the state and, at an altitude of 7,200 feet, it is the highest university in the country. One-third of Laramie's population consists of university students. Around the university, one finds boutiques, bars, and independently owned restaurants.

Laramie is faced with a disturbing large gap between rich and poor. While those who attend the university are financially secure, 15% of the native population lives below the poverty line. As Tom Johnson of the Laramie economic development corporation stated, "Laramie is one of the poorest communities in the state." Largely because of this economic gap, Laramie is plagued with a high rate of crime, substance abuse, school disciplinary problems, domestic violence, suicide, and a basic lack of opportunities for its youth.

Local Environment

Essential Questions: *What two general areas of your study site have the best population density and land use for a power plant? Why?*

Overview

This lesson will introduce you to the geographic location of your study area (as assigned to you by your teacher). Your task is to assess the area's potential for supporting each type of alternative power plant: hydroelectric, solar, wind, biomass, and nuclear. You want to find as much evidence as possible for your assessment of each type of power plant type. This lesson will aid you in making your presentation of your recommendation for the type of alternative power plant that should be built in your study area. Note that your study area does not cover the entire state. Your study area is the area shown in ArcView that includes the city and parts of the surrounding countryside. Anywhere within the study area is close enough to provide power for the nearby cities. In class today, you will become more familiar with your study site's population and land use.

Materials

 ArcView 3.2 installed on a Windows computer

 Alternative Energy project file
File name: alternatives.apr
File type: ArcView Project

Procedure 1: The ArcView Project

1. Open the Alternative Energy project file in ArcView according to your teacher's instructions.

2. You should see the view, *United States*. Find your assigned study area.

3. Under the **Window** menu, select the state for your study area (see Figure 1).

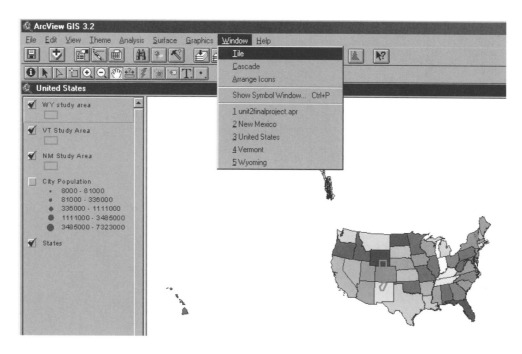

Figure 1: The Window menu, to locate the specific study area

4. Make a table that lists all the themes available in this project, their units, and a description of what they measure.

Stop and Think #1

Which themes contain information that will be useful for identifying potential alternative energy sources in your region?

Procedure 2: Assessing Population Density

1. Turn off all of the themes except the following: Study Area, City Boundaries, Roads, and Population Density.

2. In your notebook, describe the population distribution in your study area. Which areas have the greatest population density? Which have the least?

Stop and Think #2

If you were to build a power plant with the least impact on where people live, where would be the best choice?

Procedure 3: Assessing Land Use and Elevation

1. Turn off all themes except Study Area, Land Use, and City Boundaries.

2. <u>Record</u> the most common land use.

3. Turn off the Land Use theme and turn on the Elevation theme. <u>Describe</u> in a few sentences what this area looks like. Is it mountainous? Is it flat? Are the mountains near the cities?

Stop and Think #3

Switch back and forth between Land Use and Elevation. Do you see any correlation between the two? Describe it.

Analysis Questions

1. What would be the benefits of locating the power plant close to where people live? What would be the disadvantages of doing this?

2. What type of land use would be the easiest to build a power plant on?

3. How will the elevation (or lack of elevation) affect your choice of where to build a power plant?

4. Answer the essential questions: *What two general areas of your study site have the best population density and land use for a power plant? Why?*

Constraints

Essential Question: *What are the constraints for selecting a type of power for your location?*

Overview

It is important to think about decisions in terms of constraints and considerations. They can help you make sense of a complicated problem where many factors affect your final choice. Constraints describe the limitations you must work under. They may be either physical limitations or limitations that come from your personal values. For example, if there are only certain resources available to you, that would be a physical constraint. If you are unwilling to destroy the habitat of a threatened species, that would be a values-based constraint. Some constraints are time, money, laws, or environmental impacts.

Constraints are absolute limitations. They cannot be violated in a solution. Considerations are preferences that might or might not be possible. Decision makers try to achieve the most important considerations. They also keep in mind their constraints as they consider all available options.

Procedure

Determine your constraints and considerations in relation to this project. Make a list of each.

Analysis Questions

1. What is your ultimate goal for this project?

2. In an ideal world, what would you consider a successful outcome?

3. What personal values do you hold that will affect what you put on your considerations list?

4. Answer the essential question: *What are the constraints related to selecting a type of power for your location?*

Group Constraints and Considerations

 Essential Question: What made some considerations more important than others?

Overview

When environmental decisions need to be made, there are usually groups of people with very different ideas about the problem and how to solve it. In this final project for Unit 2, you will need to work with your group to make a decision you can all agree on.

Each person in your group has his or her own lists of constraints and considerations. Some items on your lists will be the same and some will be different. Your task today is to agree on a list that will guide your group through the rest of the project. This may be a difficult process. However, it is important to agree now on your goals before you continue with the Environmental Decision Making Process.

Materials

1. lists of personal constraints and considerations from each group member (from Lesson 1: *Alternative Energy Summary*)

2. letter from Lesson 1: *Alternative Energy Summary*.

Procedure

You must reach a group consensus about the constraints and considerations you will use to make your decision. Remember that constraints are goals that you must reach or rules that you must not violate. Considerations are goals you would like to achieve, but are not absolutely necessary.

Analysis Questions

1. What are the constraints that your group agrees should not be violated in this project?

2. What are the considerations that you would all like to achieve in this project?

3. Rank your group's list of considerations from most to least important.

4. Answer the essential question with at least a two-paragraph justification of your ranking. *What made some considerations more important than others?*

Lesson 3

Researching the Options

Driving Question: Which alternatives make sense for each location?

Overview

In this lesson, you will review each alternative energy source. You will complete a detailed analysis of the consequences of using each at your location. You will use ArcView to gather and analyze data about each location. Cascading Consequence Charts will help you organize the impacts of the consequences of each option. Keep in mind what you have learned in other chapters in this unit. You have information about the impacts of fossil fuels, global warming, even the basics of how electricity works. Use that information as evidence to support your decisions.

Important Content

- Each energy generation option has positive and negative impacts. Considering all of these is important in making a balanced decision.

- The area affected by a power plant is larger than the power plant itself. In fact, a power plant can have impacts over hundreds of miles. The size the impact is depends on environmental factors.

Wind Energy

? ***Essential Questions:*** *Is it feasible to have a wind farm in this area? If yes, what are the top two sites for a wind farm, and why? If no, explain why not?*

Background

Wind turbines vary in size and in the amount of power they are capable of generating. For example, a 10 kW turbine usually has a 7-meter rotor diameter. A utility-scale turbine with a 0.750 MW generating capacity has a rotor diameter of 24 meters and is mounted on a tower 63 meters high. A 1.5 MW turbine operates with a windmill that has a 70-meter rotor diameter.

In this activity, the turbines you will analyze are rated at 1 MW each. What does that mean? A turbine that is rated at 1 MW can produce that much power at maximum wind speed. If the wind is not blowing hard enough, the turbine will produce less than 1 MW. See the graph in Figure 1.

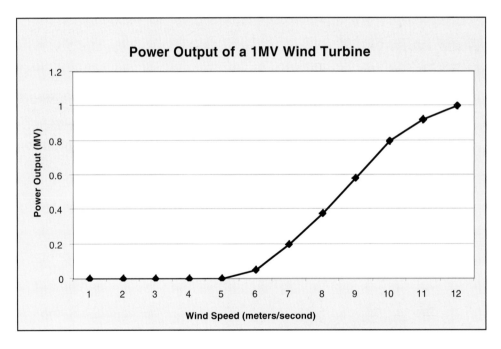

Figure 1: Power Output of a 1 MW Wind Turbine

On flat, clear land, a single 1 MW turbine requires 202,344 m² of land. However, only about 5% of that space (10,117 m²) is occupied by turbines and other equipment. The remaining land can be used for other activities, such as farming or ranching. If the turbine is located on top of a ridge or hill, it only requires 8094 m² of land.

Procedure

1. Open the Alternative Energy ArcView project according to your teacher's instructions.

2. Turn off all themes except Wind Speed. Record the highest wind speed in your study area.

3. Use the graph on the previous page. Determine the power output of each turbine at that wind speed. Record the outputs on your data sheet.

4. Use the Area tool (see instructions at the end of this lesson) to trace the outline of the power plant area with the highest wind speed. Record the area from the bottom right corner of the screen.

5. Turn off the Wind Speed theme and turn on Land Use. If necessary, re-trace the power plant to avoid urban areas and forests. Record the new area.

6. Turn off the Land Use theme and turn on the Population Density theme. If necessary, re-trace the power plant to avoid areas of high population density. Record the new area.

7. Use the Elevation theme to determine if your power plant is located in a flat area or on a ridge.

8. Calculate how many turbines will fit in the power plant area you traced. Remember that turbines need 202,344 m^2 of land if the area is flat or 8094 m^2 on top of a ridge.

9. Calculate the amount of power that you could generate by covering the entire area you selected with wind turbines. (Use the answers to Procedure Steps 3 and 8 to answer this.)

Analysis Questions

1. What is the maximum wind speed in your study area?

2. How much power can each turbine produce at that wind speed?

3. How many turbines will you need in order to generate 100 MW total?

4. How much land area will you need for the wind farm?

5. Answer the essential questions: *Is it feasible to have a wind farm in this area? If yes, what are the top two sites for a wind farm, and why? If no, explain why not?*

6. Make a Cascading Consequence Chart for your best wind power location.

Using the area tool

1. Select the Area tool from the toolbar

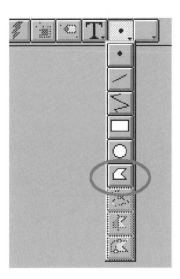

2. Click the mouse to draw
    the shape you want

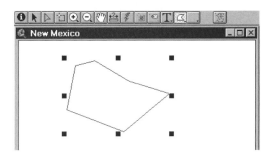

3. To change the shape, click the open
    arrow and drag the corners until
    the shape looks the way you
    want it to.

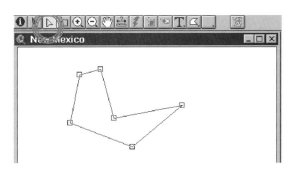

4. To delete a shape, select the closed arrow, click on the shape, and hit the delete key on your keyboard.

5. The area of the shape you drew will be in the lower right side of the screen.

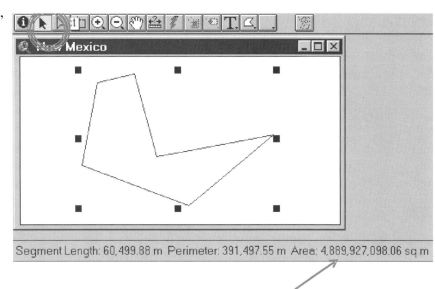

Segment Length: 60,499.88 m Perimeter: 391,497.55 m Area: 4,889,927,098.06 sq m

Biomass Energy

? *Essential Questions: Is it feasible to have a biomass power plant in this area? If yes, what are the top two sites for a biomass power plant, and why? If no, explain why not?*

Background

Biomass energy can be generated from a number of different sources, such as trees, grasses, crop waste, or garbage. For this activity, your biomass plant will run on trees grown on farm land for 7 years or on forest trees grown for 30 years. Both will be harvested as whole trees.

Biomass power plants burning whole trees at 35% efficiency would require about 4,000,000 m² of farm-grown trees per megawatt of power produced. The farmland would include mature trees that are ready to be harvested, as well as trees in all stages of growth. If there is little or no farmland, forest trees may be considered. However, because growth is much slower, assume 16,000,000 m² is required to adequately supply 1 MW. Only 1/30 of the forest area would be harvested each year.

This aerial view of a hybrid poplar test plantation in Howard Lake, Minnesota, shows tree growth after two years. Typically, such crops can be harvested after seven years of growth, at which time trees are 15 m tall. New tree crops can be planted on fields that have been harvested, or trees can be allowed to grow naturally from the remaining stumps.

Procedure

1. Open the ArcView project "**alternatives.apr**" according to your teacher's instructions.

2. Turn off all themes except Land Use. Record the two main types of land use in your study area.

3. Use the area tool to trace an area of farmland that could be used to generate biomass. Then use the area tool to trace the area of forest that could be harvested.

4. Turn on the national parks theme. If this overlaps the forest area you selected, re-draw the area so it does not include the park. <u>Record</u> the new area.

5. Turn off all themes except the population theme. Re-trace both the farmland and forest areas to avoid densely populated areas.

6. Turn off all themes except elevation. Trees high in the mountains are not very accessible and will cost more money to harvest and transport. Re-draw the area to avoid areas in the mountains.

7. Record the area in m^2 from the bottom left of the computer screen.

8. Use the following formula to <u>calculate</u> how much power could be generated by that much land with biomass power.

$$\text{Power generated (MW)} = \frac{\text{acres of farmland available in } m^2}{4,000,000 \ m^2} + \frac{\text{acres of forest land available in } m^2}{16,000,000 \ m^2}$$

Analysis Questions

1. How much power can be generated through biomass by the land available?

2. How do you think the community would react to converting cropland to production of trees or harvesting trees in existing forests for the biomass power plant?

3. How accessible are the forests? (Trees in mountainous areas are more difficult to harvest than trees in flat areas.)

4. Answer the essential questions: *Is it feasible to have a biomass power plant in this area? If yes, what are the top two sites for a biomass power plant, and why? If no, explain why not.*

5. Make a Cascading Consequence Chart for your best biomass power location.

Hydroelectric Energy

? *Essential Questions: Is it feasible to have a hydroelectric power plant in this area? If yes, what are the top two sites for a hydroelectric power plant, and why? If no, explain why not?*

Background

Hydroelectric power plants require a flowing river and a place to create a reservoir behind the dam. The reservoir will probably be a valley with high sides and an exit point for the river. This exit point is where the dam will be placed. The dam can only be as tall as the sides of the valley. A tall dam will generate more power than a short dam on the same stream.

Calculation

power generated (MW) = 0.0059 x river flow rate (m³/sec) x height of dam (m)

Procedure

1. Open the ArcView project "**alternatives.apr**" according to your teacher's instructions.

2. Turn off all themes except Contours of Elevation and Rivers. To have a suitable place for a dam, you need an elevation change and an adequate sized river. The river also needs a flow rate greater than 1m³/second. <u>Record</u> the names of rivers in your study area that pass through hilly or mountainous areas.

3. Concentrate on the rivers you counted in Step 2. Look for areas of low elevation surrounded by higher elevation –"C" or "V" shapes in the contours. This will be the reservoir behind the dam.

4. Choose one reservoir location. Using the Area tool, trace the area that you think would be flooded by the reservoir.

5. Turn off all themes except Population. <u>Record</u> the number of people who will be affected by the reservoir.

6. Turn of all themes except Land Use. <u>Record</u> the major land use type that will be flooded by the reservoir.

7. Use the equation below. Calculate the amount of power generated by building a dam in this location. (The height of the dam is the difference between the lowest contour line in the reservoir and the highest.)

power generated (MW) = 0.0059 x river flow rate (m^3/sec) x height of dam (m)

Analysis Questions

1. What type of land use will be flooded by creating the reservoir?

2. Is the river flow rate and dam height sufficient to generate the power you need?

3. What do you think the public's reaction would be to a dam being built in their area?

4. Answer the essential questions: *Is it feasible to have a hydroelectric power plant in this area? If yes, what are the top two sites for a hydroelectric power plant, and why? If no, explain why not?*

5. Make a Cascading Consequence Chart for your best hydroelectric power location.

Solar Energy

?

Essential Questions: Is it feasible to have a solar power plant in this area? If yes, what are the top two sites for a solar power plant, and why? If no, explain why not?

Overview

Solar power plants have many advantages over other forms of power generation. However, they also make unique demands on the environment and geography. In this activity, you will determine the best places to site a photovoltaic solar power plant in your region.

Background

Solar power can be collected in different ways, including photovoltaic panels and heat-concentrators. Photovoltaic, or PV, panels are what you see on the roofs of houses or other small buildings. In the past, their average efficiency rate has only been about 8%. However, improved technology has recently boosted PV efficiency to 18.3%. More research and innovation will certainly increase PV efficiency even more in the future. Larger utility-scale solar power plants are usually heat concentrators, not PV. Concentrators are much more efficient than PV at about 16%. In comparison, coal-burning power plants have efficiency of about 36%; and with new technology can reach 42%.

Since you are building a utility-scale plant, you should use the more efficient form of collection, heat-concentrating troughs.

The heat-concentrating troughs of this system must be close together, in a square or rectangular formation. The land must be flat and open to the south. This direction gets the greatest amount of direct sunlight in the Northern Hemisphere.

Procedure

1. Open the ArcView project "**alternatives.apr**" according to your teacher's instructions.

2. Turn off all themes except Incoming Solar Energy. Record the highest value for incoming solar energy in your study area. (Some areas have only one value for incoming solar energy. In this case, record the one value.)

3. Use the Area tool to trace an area of high incoming solar energy that could be used to build a solar power plant.

4. Turn off all themes except Land Use. Record the type of land use that is most common in the solar power plant.

5. Turn off all themes except Population. Re-draw your outline to avoid heavily populated areas.

6. Record the area that you have outlined.

7. Turn off all themes except Aspect. This shows the direction the land is facing. Estimate and record how much of your selected area is facing south or flat.

8. Use the following formula to calculate how much power could be generated by that much land with solar power. Be careful with units. Remember that 1 MW = 1,000,000 W.

    solar energy (W/m^2) x 16% efficiency x area (m^2) = amount of power generated in W

    Then, convert Watts to Megawatts:
    power in watts /1,000,000 = power in megawatts

Analysis Questions

1. What type of land use would you build your solar power plant on? What advantages and disadvantages will this have?

2. How many people will be affected by the solar power plant?

3. Is it possible to generate enough energy from solar power in your study area?

4. Answer the essential questions: *Is it feasible to have a solar power plant in this area? If yes, what are the top two sites for a solar power plant, and why? If no, explain why not?*

5. Make a Cascading Consequence Chart for your best solar power location.

Nuclear Energy

Essential Questions: *Is it feasible to have a nuclear power plant in this area? If yes, what are the top two sites for a nuclear power plant, and why? If no, explain why not?*

Background

Many of the parts in a nuclear power plant are similar to those in a fossil-fuel burning power plant. The main difference is that the steam boiler is replaced by a Nuclear Steam Supply System (NSSS). The NSSS consists of a nuclear reactor and all of the parts needed to produce high-pressure steam. The steam again is used to turn the turbine for the electrical generator.

Like a fossil-fuel power plant, a nuclear power plant boils water to produce electricity. Unlike a fossil-fuel plant, the nuclear plant's energy does not come from the combustion of fuel. It comes from the fission, or splitting, of atoms.

Uranium is the most common fuel used in nuclear power plants in the U.S. Uranium is a mineral ore, and it is mined like other ores. Because it exists in limited quantities, uranium is not a renewable resource, as wind, solar, and biomass are. Being non-renewable is something nuclear power has in common with fossil fuel power. Mined uranium contains a very low percentage, or enrichment, of the uranium atoms (U-235) that can be used in nuclear reactors. It is made up mostly of unusable U-238 atoms. The process that increases the number of U-235 atoms is called the enrichment process and turns ore into fuel. Once the fuel has been enriched, it is turned into pellets. The pellets are stacked into 12-foot long, slender metal tubes. When a tube is filled with the uranium pellets, it is pressurized with helium gas. Plugs are then installed and welded to seal it. The filled tube is called a "fuel rod." Fuel rods are bundled together into "fuel assemblies" or "fuel elements." The completed assemblies are shipped to nuclear power plants for installation into the nuclear reactor.

All steam plants, nuclear or fossil fuel, need a circulating water system to remove excess heat from the steam system. This condenses the steam and transfers that heat to the environment. The circulating water system pumps water from the environment (river, lake, or ocean) through thousands of metal tubes in the plant's condenser. Steam released from the plant's turbine is very rapidly cooled and condensed into water when it comes in contact with the much cooler tubes. Since the tubes provide a barrier between the steam and the environment, there is no physical contact between the plant's steam and the cooling water. So, the water vapor coming out of the cooling tower is NOT radioactive.

The fuel rods used in nuclear power plants have a limited life span. Eventually, they must be discarded even though they are still dangerously radioactive. Spent fuel from nuclear power plants is toxic for thousands of years. As of yet, there is no safe permanent storage facility for this fuel. Congress is considering an underground storage site beneath Yucca Mountain in Nevada, but the issue is very controversial. Transporting nuclear fuel to and from power plants also poses some risks. Fortunately, the U.S. safety record has been good so far.

Procedure

1. Open the ArcView project "**alternatives.apr**" according to your teacher's instructions.

2. Turn off all themes except Land Use and Roads.

3. Find all lakes within 2500 meters of a highway or interstate. (Use the Measure tool to find the distance from the lake to the road.)

4. Which of the lakes you chose in Step 2 are also at least 2500 meters or farther away from the nearest residential area?

Analysis Questions

1. How many lakes in your study area are close to roads AND far from residential areas?

2. Is there an appropriate place in your state to store the radioactive waste produced by the power plant? If not, what will you do with it?

3. Answer the essential questions: *Is it feasible to have a nuclear power plant in this area? If yes, what are the top two sites for a nuclear power plant, and why? If no, explain why not?*

4. Make a Cascading Consequence Chart for your best nuclear power location.

Narrowing Options

Essential Question: *How do the three choices fit the constraints and considerations YOU feel are most important?*

Overview

In this activity, you will compare the options you researched throughout Lesson 3. With your group, you will need to reach consensus about which three options are best. (The three options that you choose should be very different from each other.) As you discuss the different options, remember to use evidence to support your viewpoint. Use the readings from earlier in the chapter to better understand the environmental consequences of each alternative. Use your group list of constraints and considerations to guide your choices and eliminate unsuitable options.

Procedure

With your group, discuss the options that were developed. Select the three best possibilities. Use the consequence charts to help you make your group decision. Make sure that the options chosen meet your constraints and considerations.

Analysis Questions

1. For each of the three options, your group should put together:

    a. a sketch or complete description of the type of power plant you chose and the placement on the map.

    b. a Cascading Consequence Chart that describes consequences to the environment, and the community. The charts should include answers to questions like:

        i.   What types of land are being covered by the power plant? What effect will that have on the natural environment?

        ii. What other kinds of land/cities will be affected by the emissions and waste products of the power plant?

        iii. What effects will the placement of the power plant have on the residents who live in the immediate area?

2. Answer the essential question: *How do the three choices fit the constraints and considerations YOU feel are most important?*

Lesson 4
Decision

Driving Question: *Which of the options has the smallest number of unintended consequences?*

Overview

Use the consequence charts from the last lesson to continue exploring the consequences of your power plant choice. With your team, you will identify your *stakeholders* and determine how important they are to your decision. To organize this information, you will use the Stakeholders Chart from the environmental decision making process. This chart will help you see how different stakeholders will be affected by your actions, so you can make your decision and present it to your classmates. You have reached the end! All of your information is gathered. You know the consequences of each option before you. All that is left is to make the choice and justify it with an explanation. In this lesson, you will work with your group to select the best option and explain your decision to your classmates. Use all of the information you have gathered in this chapter and unit to explain your decision. Use your constraints and considerations, and your knowledge of power plants and their environmental impacts. In your final presentation, show that you understand the effects of electrical power production on our environment.

Important Content

*   When determining the best way to generate electricity for a community, it is important to look at the available local resources.

*   The area affected by a power plant is larger than the power plant itself. In fact, a power plant can have impacts over hundreds of miles, depending on environmental factors and local population density.

Investigate Impacts

Essential Questions: *Which stakeholders will be most affected by your decision? Are those stakeholders the ones who have the power to make the decision?*

Overview

You now have proposals and consequence charts for your three options. It is time to look more closely at consequences. In today's activity, you will construct stakeholder charts for the options you chose in the last lesson. Stakeholders are people, organizations, the environment, etc, that will be affected by your decision. The chart you make in this activity will help you to organize the consequences in a different way. It will give you a picture of all the ways that each stakeholder will be affected. It is important to note whether the effect is your intended goal or a side effect. Decisions with many unintended side effects might not be the best ones to make. A second part of side effects and negative effects in general is consent. Did the stakeholder consent to be a part of this process or decision? Think about the responsibilities decision makers have for the consequences of their actions.

Procedure

1. Create a list of stakeholders based on your consequence charts and research.

2. As a group, complete the stakeholders chart for each of the options.

Analysis Questions

1. How did you narrow your list of stakeholders?

2. How are the stakeholders related to your list of constraints and criteria?

3. Do you believe that decision makers are responsible for the unintended effects of the decisions that they make? Why or why not?

4. Answer the essential questions: *Which stakeholders will be most affected by your decision? Are those stakeholders the ones who have the power to make the decision?*

Stakeholders for Option #1

Who are the stakeholders that will be affected by this action?	In what way(s) will they be affected?	+ or –	Is this effect the intended goal of the action or is it a side effect?	Has the stakeholders placed themselves in this position voluntarily and with appropriate understanding of the risks involved?	How important to YOU are the interests of this stakeholder? 1=very important 2= somewhat important 3=unimportant	If the effect is negative, do YOU feel it is directly offset by greater good elsewhere?

Stakeholders for Option #2

Who are the stakeholders that will be affected by this action?	In what way(s) will they be affected?	+ or –	Is this effect the intended goal of the action or is it a side effect?	Has the stakeholders placed themselves in this position voluntarily and with appropriate understanding of the risks involved?	How important to YOU are the interests of this stakeholder? 1=very important 2= somewhat important 3=unimportant	If the effect is negative, do YOU feel it is directly offset by greater good elsewhere?

Stakeholders for Option #3

Who are the stakeholders that will be affected by this action?	In what way(s) will they be affected?	+ or –	Is this effect the intended goal of the action or is it a side effect?	Has the stakeholders placed themselves in this position voluntarily and with appropriate understanding of the risks involved?	How important to YOU are the interests of this stakeholder? 1=very important 2= somewhat important 3=unimportant	If the effect is negative, do YOU feel it is directly offset by greater good elsewhere?

Make a Decision

Essential Question: *Taking into account all stakeholders, consequences, constraints, and considerations, what is the best decision?*

Analysis Question

1. Answer the essential question: *Taking into account all stakeholders, consequences, constraints, and considerations, what is the best decision?*

    Make sure to address each criteria and consideration you listed.

    Make sure to explain how any negative effects are outweighed by the positive effects.

Present Your Decision

Essential Question: *What were the major obstacles to this decision?*

Overview

An important part of environmental decisions is supporting your claims with evidence. As you prepare your report and presentation, remember you are trying to convince people why your decision is the best one. Use evidence from the rest of Unit 2 to support your opinions. Describe logically why you made the decisions that you made. Give the reasons why you rejected some options. Include your values and opinions in the decision, but make sure to back up what you are saying with facts, evidence, and logic.

Procedure

Compile a report that includes:

1. a list of your group constraints and considerations

2. a complete description of the three best options

3. consequence charts and stakeholder charts for all three options

4. a decision statement that describes how you met each constraint and consideration

Answer the analysis questions below.

Give a 5-minute presentation that includes:

1. a map of your chosen option

2. a summary of why you chose the option you did

Analysis Questions

1. Are you satisfied with your decision? Why or why not?

2. Is there anything you would change if you had the chance to make the decision again?

3. Answer the essential question: *What were the major obstacles to this decision?*

Glossary

Absorbed solar energy – sunlight that is taken in and retained by a substance and converted to heat energy

Acid deposition – occurs as wet and dry deposition; wet deposition (or "acid rain") where SO_2 and NO_x compounds bind with water to acidify rain, snow or fog AND dry deposition when acidic gases and particles naturally fall to the ground

Acid rain – when sulfuric acid (SO_2) and nitric acid (NO_x) are oxidized in atmosphere, they react with water, oxygen, and other chemicals to form acids that fall as rain. Sunlight increases the rate of most of these reactions.

Albedo – the reflective quality of the earth and atmosphere; also called "earth-atmosphere reflectivity"

Algae blooms – uncontrolled growth of algae in water bodies

Aspect – the direction the slope of the ground is facing; important in the placement of solar panels because a southern or flat aspect will collect the most sunlight

Atmosphere – the thin blanket of air that encircles the planet

Atom – the smallest portion an element can be divided into and still retain its properties; made up of a dense, positively charged nucleus surrounded by a system of electrons. Atoms are identified by the number of protons they contain.

Auroras – light emissions that occur when partly neutral and partly ionized gases return to their original state after being excited by the solar wind (made up of mostly protons and electrons)

Bioaccumulation – the ingestion and storage of toxins in body tissue

Biomass – any kind of organic matter located within the layer of living systems around the planet

Biomass power – the production of power by the burning of plants (trees, paper, lumberyard or agricultural waste, etc.); also created by burning clean municipal wastes and sludge

Blackout – a temporary power outage or loss of electricity to a building or area

Brownout – a temporary reduction in electrical power caused by high consumer demand or by technical malfunction

Buffer – a zone of specified distance around a feature on a map; used to evaluate what is close to another object on a map

Calorie – the amount of heat required to raise the temperature of 1.0 g of water 1°C. One calorie (cal) equals 4.18 joules (J).

Calorimeter – an apparatus used to measure the amount of energy evolved or absorbed in a chemical or physical process

Carbon dioxide – (CO_2) a colorless, odorless, non-poisonous gas that is a normal part of the air. CO_2 is exhaled by humans and animals and is absorbed by green growing things and the sea.

Carbon monoxide – (CO) an odorless, colorless gas that interferes with the delivery of oxygen from the blood to the body and is very important in the chemistry of the lower atmosphere. CO is produced by the incomplete combustion of fuels and also by chemical reactions with hydrocarbons in the atmosphere.

Charge – a fundamental characteristic of matter, responsible for all electric forces; expressed in two forms known as positive and negative

Chemical Energy – energy involved in rearranging atoms or molecules, resulting in the creation or destruction of a chemical compound

Circuit – a route through which an electrical current can flow, beginning and ending at the same point

Closed-cycle – systems discharge heat through evaporation in cooling towers and recycle the water within the power plant

Coal seam – coal that is found under ground in large areas in a horizontal band

Coalification (carbonization) – the process that alters peat. The process involves decaying of dead plants, decomposition by bacteria, compaction under layers of soil and other dead plants, heat, and time.

Combustion – burning or rapid oxidation combined with the release of heat and light energy

Compound – something made by the chemical combination of two or more different elements

Conductor – a substance, body, or medium that allows electricity to pass along it or through it. Metals are good conductors of electricity because they contain a high concentration of free electrons.

Congeneration – the simultaneous production of electricity and useful heat from the same fuel; is also called "combined heat and power"

Correlation – the degree to which attributes of the same group of elements show a tendency to vary together

Current – the flow of electrons from a region of high electrical charge to low electrical charge

Dam – a barrier preventing the flow of water or of loose solid materials

Density – mass per unit volume ($D = m/v$)

Deposition – (as it relates to air quality) the process of particles falling out of the air onto the ground or water

Desertification – degradation of formerly productive land

Dissolved Oxygen – the amount of oxygen in water. Cold water can hold more oxygen than warmer water.

Efficiency – the ratio of useful energy delivered by a dynamic system to the energy supplied to it

Efficient – productive of desired effects; productive without waste

Electrical energy – energy involved in the movement of electrons

Electron – a stable, negatively-charged elementary particle with a very small mass that is a fundamental constituent of matter; found in orbit around the nucleus of an atom

Element – any substance that cannot be broken down into a simpler substance by a chemical reaction

Emission Standards – regulations that set limits on the release of air pollutants into the atmosphere

Emissions – something that is produced or given out; substances discharged into the air (as by a smokestack or a gasoline engine)

Eutrophication – the process in which excessive amounts of nutrients (particularly nitrogen and phosphorus) enter a body of water, causing an explosion in the populations of aquatic plants; will eventually result in depleted levels of dissolved oxygen in the water

Fix – the process by which an organism takes carbon dioxide from the air and incorporates it into its body system. Trees fix carbon from carbon dioxide in the air into useful sugars.

Floodplain – an area of low-lying land across which a river flows that is covered with sediment as a result of frequent flooding

Flux – continuous change, passage, or movement

Generator – a machine or device that is used to convert mechanical energy (like the energy provided by a spinning turbine shaft) into electricity

Global warming – an average increase in the earth's temperature, which in turn causes changes in climate

Greenhouse effect – a condition where greenhouse gases (e.g., carbon dioxide) make the earth warmer by trapping heat in the atmosphere

Ground-level ozone – "bad" ozone found at ground level is a pollutant; created by photochemical reactions involving air, NO_2, and sunlight

Hardness – a measure of a mineral's resistance to abrasion; related to the atomic structure of a mineral

Heat energy – energy involved in changing temperature

Hybrid power – combining two or more alternative energies (e.g., biomass, wind, solar, and hydroelectric) into one that provides a more constant energy supply

Hydroelectric power – the process by which the kinetic energy in flowing water is used to spin a turbine connected to a generator to produce electricity

Ice Core – samples of ice than can be obtained from glaciers or ice sheets that give scientists information about past weather and atmosphere conditions

Infrared radiation (also known as long-wave radiation) – thermal or heat radiation, a wavelength longer than visible light

Insolation (not to be confused with "insulation") – the scientific term for incoming solar radiation

Insulator – a material or device that prevents or reduces the passage of electricity

Ionosphere – portion of the mesosphere and thermosphere where auroras occur

Kilocalorie (kcal) – (prefix 'kilo' means 1000) 1 kcal is equivalent to 1000 calories. 1 kcal could heat up 1000g of water by 1°C.

Kilowatt-hour(s) (kWh) – a unit of energy equal to the work done by one kilowatt in one hour

Kilowatts – equivalent to 1,000 watts; a unit of power, energy per second

Light energy – energy associated with the movement of photons

Long wave radiation – electromagnetic radiation with long wavelengths; longer than visible light wavelengths but shorter than radio wavelengths

Mechanical energy – energy involved in the movement of physical objects by the application of forces or phase changes

Megawatts – 1 megawatt is equivalent to 1,000 kilowatts.

Mercury – (Hg) naturally occurs in three forms: metallic mercury (also known as elemental mercury), inorganic mercury, and organic mercury. The metal is the liquid that you see in thermometers. Most inorganic mercury compounds are white powders or crystals, except for mercuric sulfide (also known as cinnabar, mercuric sulfide is red and turns black after exposure to light). The most common organic mercury compound in the environment is methylmercury which can build up in fish to unsafe levels and be harmful to humans.

Mesosphere – the layer about 50 to 90 km above the earth which contains portions of the ionosphere. Here temperature again decreases with increasing altitude and convection can occur.

Methane – (CH_4) a colorless, odorless gas with a wide distribution in nature; is the principal component of natural gas. It is also a greenhouse gas and is the third contributor to climate change, after water and carbon dioxide

Micron – the unit used to measure particulates that equal a length to one-millionth of a meter (or 1/1000 of a millimeter)

Natural variation – the random fluctuation of points around a central value

Neutron – a neutral elementary particle with a zero electrical charge and a mass approximately equal to that of a proton

Nitrogen oxides – (NO_x) $NO_x = NO + NO_2$, a chief component of air pollution; produced by the burning of fossil fuels, among other sources

Nuclear energy – energy involved in breaking apart or putting together the nucleus of an atom

Nuclear power – the process of creating electricity from the energy that exists within the nucleus of an atom

Nucleus – the positively charged central portion of an atom that comprises nearly all of the atomic mass; consists of protons and neutrons (except in hydrogen which has no neutrons)

Once-through systems – require the intake from a water source with a continual flow of cooling water. Water demand for a once-through system is 30 to 50 times that of a closed cycle system.

Open pit mining – stationary mining where coal seams are larger and deeper which often results in larger, deeper pits

Oscillation – a single swing from one extreme limit to the other; a flow that periodically changes direction

Overburden – the topsoil and rock that lies on top of the coal

Oxidation – a chemical reaction in which oxygen is added to a substance

Ozone layer – layer in the stratosphere where high concentrations of ozone are found; protects the earth from most of the harmful ultraviolet radiation from the sun

Particulate – small solid particles and liquid droplets that are suspended in the air

Parts per million – the number of grams per million grams of solvent; used to measure very small quantities. Air concentration is expressed in parts per million by volume.

Percent efficiency – the ratio of the amount of energy used by a machine to the amount of work done by it

Permafrost – permanently frozen ground that underlies one-fifth of the world's land. If permafrost ground is allowed to thaw, it can lose its strength allowing structures built on it to be damaged.

Photovoltaic – a cell that can convert light directly into electricity

Plume – an area of contamination or pollution that can be found in the air or in water; often spreads from a single point into a much larger area

Precipitator – part of a power plant attached to the stack where small particles of dust and ash are removed from the released gases

Proton – a stable elementary particle that is a component of all atomic nuclei; carries a positive charge equal to that of the electron's negative charge

Radiate – to send out or emit rays

Radiation – the emission or transmission of energy

Radioactive – the property possessed by some elements (as uranium) or isotopes (as carbon-14) of spontaneously emitting energetic particles (as electrons or alpha particles) by the disintegration of their atomic nuclei

Reactor – a device for the controlled release of nuclear energy

Reflected solar energy – sunlight that is reflected by objects on Earth's surface or the atmosphere

Reflectivity – how much something reflects sunlight energy

Reservoir – an artificial lake where water is collected and kept in quantity for use

Rotor – the rotating member of an electrical machine

Scrubbers – limestone mixed with water and sprayed into coal combustion gases; acts to "pull" sulfur out of the gases. The limestone and sulfur combine to form either a wet paste, or in some new scrubbers, a dry powder.

Sediment – layers of silty soil

Shortwave radiation – radiation that comes from the sun, sunlight

Sinks – area of the environment that takes carbon dioxide from the air and stores it as carbon

Smokestack – pipe or funnel found on power plants through which smoke and gases are discharged

Solar power – the process by which energy from the sun can be directly converted into electricity by using solar cells

Spent fuel – fuel tubes full of uranium that have come to the end of their life span but are still radioactive

Stratosphere – the layer between approximately 15 km (at the equator, or 8 km at the poles) and 50 km above the earth and contains the ozone layer. Temperature here increases with increasing altitude.

Stream flow – rate at which water flows (usually in cubic meters) in a streambed

Strip mine – mining in motion where the miners remove the overburden and pile it next to the mine while following the path of the coal seam

Subsidence – a depression in the ground at the surface caused by underground mining

Sulfur dioxide – (SO_2) a colorless gas that can irritate the lungs and is a major contributor to acidic deposition when released into the atmosphere. Anthropogenic (human-made) emissions due primarily to fossil fuel combustion are much greater than the naturally occurring sources of SO_2.

Surface temperature – the degree of hotness or coldness at the surface of the earth; a measure of the amount of energy stored on the surface, determined by the amount of energy absorbed from the sun, the atmosphere, and energy trapped in the earth's interior

Thermal pollution – pollution caused by abnormally heating the air, land, or water

Thermosphere – the layer above the mesosphere where temperature increases rapidly to 250°C to 1500°C

Transmission – the movement of electricity from a power plant to the point of use, usually through wires

Transmit – to pass through an object to something else

Trend – to extend in a general direction, to follow a general course

Troposphere – the layer closest to the surface of the earth where temperature decreases with height. Lots of mixing of air masses here create and contain our weather.

Trough – a long and narrow or shallow channel or depression

Turbine – a machine in which a moving fluid such as steam acts upon the blades of a rotor to produce rotational motion that can be transformed to electrical or mechanical power

Underground mine – mining underground because the seam is too far underground to be reached with surface methods

Unintended – something that was not meant to occur

Uranium – silvery, heavy, radioactive and metallic element often used to create nuclear energy

VOCs – Volatile Organic Compounds, such as benzene and ethylene

Volume – the amount of space matter occupies

Watt (W) – international (SI) unit of power equal to 1 Joule per second; the power produced by a current of one ampere acting across a potential difference of one volt

Wetlands – marshes, swamps, or other areas of land where the soil near the surface is saturated or covered with water sometimes forming a habitat for wildlife

Wind power – the process where wind turns the blades of a windmill, which turn a shaft that powers a turbine to produce electricity

Wind speed – rate at which the wind blows. With wind power there is a minimum wind speed needed to power a turbine.

Index

A

Absorbed solar energy 212-217, 232
Acid deposition 96-97, 118, 121-122, 146
Acid rain 7, 118-124, 126, 149, 254
Albedo 195, 204, 208, 210, 213, 216, 218-220, 232
Algae blooms 135
Anthracite 42
Aspect 285
Atmosphere 10, 92, 95-98, 108, 111, 115, 118-121, 127-131, 138, 141-146, 184, 186, 190-191, 218-247
Atmospheric deposition 113
Atom 16-18, 48, 127, 260

B

Bioaccumulation 115-116
Biomass 30, 243, 259-261, 280-281
Biomass power 259-261, 280-281
Bituminous 42
Blackout 3-7, 36, 63, 67, 85, 102
Brownout 3-7, 11, 63, 85, 102
Buffer 67, 122, 167-169

C

Calorie 51-54, 71
Calorimeter 51-55, 71
Carbon dioxide 10, 59, 89, 92, 95, 97, 118, 141, 182, 186, 190, 192, 221-230, 235-246, 251, 256
Carbon monoxide 89, 95-97, 242
Carboniferous period 47
Carbonization 41
Charge 16-17
Chemical Energy 23, 31, 50, 59, 141, 227
Circuit 15, 19
Climate 6, 10, 95, 97, 160, 181-203, 210, 218-221, 228, 230, 235, 237, 242, 247-250, 254
Closed-cycle 133
Coal 31, 36-50, 54, 57-77, 89-92, 95-105, 107-108, 110-115, 121, 127-139, 146, 148-151, 154-157, 235, 242-243, 256, 284

Coal seam 43-46
Coalification 41
Cogeneration 74, 76
Combined cycle technology 75
Combustion 56, 74-75, 89-100, 113-115, 128, 148-150, 242
Conductor 17
Correlation 272
Current 15-19, 59, 218-219

D

Dam 260, 282-283
Deforestation 243
Density 39, 271-272, 289
Deposition 96-97, 113-114, 118, 121-123
Desulfurization 98
Direct deposition 113
Dissolved Oxygen 134-136
Dry deposition 96, 113, 118

E

Earth's surface temperature 213-217, 232
Earth-atmosphere reflectivity 211-214, 232
Efficiency 55, 70-77, 259, 280, 284-285
Efficient 6, 55, 70-78, 85-86
Electrical current 18
Electrical energy 29, 258
Electromagnetic radiation 226
Electron 16
Element 16, 115
Emission Standards 64
Emissions 7-8, 95-98, 105, 108, 111, 113-114, 121, 144, 148-150, 182, 242-245

F

Floodplain 9
Flux 240-241
Fossil fuel 9, 36, 47, 76, 88-89, 105, 130, 254, 261
Friction 17

G

Generator 59, 75, 92, 259-260
Glacial ice 235-236
Global warming 182-183, 186-193, 218-219, 243
Globally averaged temperature 202-203
Grand climate cycles 202
Greenhouse effect 182, 221, 226-230, 233-235
Ground-level ozone 96-97, 128, 143

H

Hardness 38-39
Heat energy 31-32, 55, 59, 74, 205
Hybrid power 261
Hydraulic mining 46
Hydrocarbons 41, 47-48, 127-128, 242-243
Hydroelectric power 30, 259-260, 282-283

I

Ice Core 239
Incoming solar energy 195, 208, 212-213, 216-217, 230, 232
Indirect deposition 113
Infrared radiation 226
Insulator 17

K

Kerogen 48
Kilocalorie (kcal) 298
Kilowatt-hour 60
Kilowatts 60, 79-80

L

Light energy 31, 205
Lignite 42
Long wave radiation 222, 227
Longwall mining 46

M

Mechanical energy 31, 59, 227
Megawatts 60, 285
Mercury 115-116
Mesosphere 141, 143

Methane 41, 48, 92, 227-228, 230, 235, 242-244
Micron 110
Mountaintop removal 43-44

N

Natural variation 195
Neutron 16
Nitrogen oxides 89, 95-98, 121, 127-128, 242
Nuclear energy 31, 260-261, 286
Nuclear power 30-31, 255, 260-261, 286-287
Nucleus 16, 260

O

Oil shale 48
Oil tar 48
Once-through 133-134
Open pit mining 43-44
Overburden 43-44
Oxidation 97
Ozone layer 128, 142-143, 244

P

Particulate 110-113, 149
Peat 40-42
Percent efficiency 73
Photochemical smog 127
Photovoltaic 31, 258, 284
Plume 144-145
Positive feedback cycle 229
Precipitator 58
Proton 16

R

Radiate 222, 227
Radiation 142-143, 220, 222, 226-230, 244, 261
Radioactive 31, 260-261, 286
Reactor 261, 286
Reflected solar energy 212-213, 232
Reflectivity 210-213, 220, 232
Reservoir 48, 240, 282-283
Reservoir rock 45
Room and pillar mining 45
Rotor 276

S

Saline 219
Scrubbers 98-100, 115, 150
Sediment 41, 47, 236, 260
Sedimentary rocks 235-236
Shortwave radiation 227
Sinks 219
Smog 97, 118, 127-129
Smokestack 113-114, 144-145
Solar energy 31, 195-196, 207-214, 227, 230, 232, 258-261, 284-285
Solar power 30, 255, 261, 284-285
Source rock 48
Spent fuel 286
Stratosphere 128, 141-143
Stream flow 218
Strip mine 44, 92
Strip mining 43-44
Sub-bituminous 42
Sulfur dioxide 89, 95-98, 118, 121, 146
Surface mining 43-45
Surface temperature 211-217, 232

T

Tar sands 48
Thermal pollution 134-135
Thermosphere 141-143
Transmission 58, 206
Transmit 205-207, 222
Trend 184, 186
Troposphere 128, 141-144
Trough 284
Turbine 56, 59, 74-75, 130-131, 150, 258-260, 276-277, 286

U

Underground mine 46
Unintended 118, 176, 290
Uranium 31, 260, 286

V

Volatile Organic Compounds [VOCs] 110, 127-128
Volume 39, 132, 134, 145

W

Washing 98
Water consumption 134
Water use 130-137
Watt (W) 60, 80, 213, 232, 285
Weather 121, 123, 142, 144, 182-183, 186-189, 196, 202, 247, 249
Wet deposition 96, 113
Wind power 258, 261
Wind speed 146-147, 276